PIECES FOR EVERY DAY
THE SCHOOLS CELEBRATE

BY

NORMA H. DEMING

Formerly Principal of Horace Mann School,
Minneapolis, Minnesota

AND

KATHARINE I. BEMIS

Teacher of English, Franklin Junior High School,
Minneapolis, Minnesota

NOBLE AND NOBLE, *Publishers*

76 FIFTH AVENUE   NEW YORK

PREFACE

The many commemorative occasions observed in our schools justify the compilation of material in this volume.

On teachers devolve the duty and necessity of finding selections appropriate for each " Special Day " as it approaches on the calendar. To many this is only " another task " added to the already over-crowded curriculum of our present system of education. To such teachers we trust this volume will prove a blessing and a source of pleasure.

It has been our endeavor to include in this compilation selections of high literary value and of ennobling sentiment that shall stimulate a greater love and reverence for these occasions.

While some old selections have been included because they are indelibly linked to these anniversaries by tradition, our aim has been to present for the most part *new* and *fresh material* which hitherto has not been assembled in any similar volume. Hence appear numerous poems from current literature, that reflect the sentiment of the more recent writers.

We desire to especially emphasize the selections for Roosevelt Day, Red Cross Day, Constitution Day, and Mothers' Day.

This compilation would have been impossible were it not that both authors and publishers have so cordially and generously given us permission to use copyright material.

Many letters testify to their hearty co-operation and expression of pleasure in contributing to our effort. To these we bear a deep feeling of indebtedness and gratitude.—

Norma H. Deming.
Katharine I. Bemis.

CONTENTS

New Year's Day

Lincoln's Birthday

Washington's Birthday

Contents

Contents

Mothers' Day

Memorial Day

Contents

Contents

Contents

Contents

A BRIGHT New Year and a sunny track
   Along an upward way,
And a song of praise on looking back,
   When the year has passed away,
And golden sheaves, nor small, nor few!
This is my New Year's wish for you!

NEW YEAR'S DAY

January 1

From very ancient times the first day of the new year has been observed as a holy festival. It is referred to in the Bible as the Feast of the Trumpets. The ancient Romans also celebrated this day with pagan festivities.

New Year's Day

Anonymous

O GLAD New Year! O glad New Year!
Dawn brightly on us all,
And bring us hope, our hearts to cheer,
Whatever may befall.
On thee, Old Year, O past Old Year!
Our lingering looks we cast,
Ere thou dost all our actions bear
Into the shadowy past.

For all the joy and happiness
To us this past year given,
For all the love and blessedness,
For all good gifts from Heaven:
For all the care, and sadness, too,
And hearts by sorrow riven,
As well as for all gladness true —
Our highest thanks be given.

" Life passes — passes " like a dream —
And yet we, looking back,
See many a golden, sunny gleam
Upon the Old Year's track;
And, looking forward, can we doubt
That there shall yet be gleams
Of sunshine o'er us, and about
Us many radiant beams?

Then welcome, welcome, glad New Year!
Dawn brightly on us all,
And bring us hope, our hearts to cheer,
Whatever may befall;
Bring patience, comfort, gladness, rest;
Bring blessings from above;
Bring happiness — the highest, best —
To us and those we love.

A New Year

Margaret E. Sangster

WHY do we greet thee, O blithe New Year!
What are thy pledges of mirth and cheer?
Comest, knight-errant, the wrong to right?
Comest to scatter our gloom with light?
Wherefore the thrill, the sparkle and shine,
In heart and eyes at a word of thine?

The old was buoyant, the old was true,
The old was brave when the old was new.
He crowned us often with grace and gift:
His sternest skies had a deep blue rift.
Straight and swift, when his hand unclasped,
With welcome and joyance thine we grasped.
O tell us, Year — we are fain to know —
What is thy charm that we hail thee so?

Dost promise much that is fair and sweet —
The wind's low stir in the rippling wheat,
The wave's soft plash on the sandy floor,
The bloom of roses from shore to shore,
Glance of wings from the bowery nest,

Music and perfume from east to west,
Frosts to glitter in jeweled rime,
Blush of sunrise at morning's prime,
Stars above us their watch to keep,
And rain and dew, though we wake or sleep!

Once more a voice, and I hear it call
Like a bugle-note from a mountain wall;
The pines uplift it with mighty sound,
The billows bear it the green earth round;
A voice that rolls in a jubilant song,
A conqueror's ring in its echo strong;
Through the ether clear, from the solemn sky
The New Year beckons, and makes reply;

" I bring you, friends, what the years have brought
Since ever men toiled, aspired, or thought —
Days for labor, and nights for rest;
And I bring you love, a heaven-born guest;
Space to work in, and work to do,
And faith in that which is pure and true.
Hold me in honor and greet me dear,
And sooth you'll find me a Happy Year."

The New Year

George Cooper

A SONG for the Old,
While its knell is tolled,
And its parting moments fly!
But a song and a cheer
For the glad New Year,

While we watch the Old Year die!
   Oh! its grief and pain
   Ne'er can come again,
And its care lies buried deep;
   But what joy untold
   Doth the New Year hold,
And what hopes within it sleep!

   A song for the Old,
   While its knell is tolled,
And the friends it gave so true!
   But, with hearts of glee,
   Let us merrily
Welcome in the bright, bright New!
   For the heights we gained,
   For the good attained,
We will not the Old despise;
   But a joy more sweet,
   Making life complete,
In the golden New Year lies.

   A song for the Old,
   While its knell is tolled!
With a grander, broader zeal,
   And a forward view,
   Let us greet the New,
Heart and purpose ever leal!
   Let the ills we met,
   And the sad regret,
With the Old be buried deep;
   For what joy untold
   Doth the New Year hold,
And what hopes within it sleep.

Address to the New Year

Dinah Mulock Craik

O GOOD New Year! we clasp
  This warm, shut hand of thine,
Loosing forever, with half sigh, half grasp,
  That which from ours falls like dead fingers'
    twine.
Ay, whether fierce its grasp
Has been, or gentle, having been, we know
That it was blessed; let the old year go.

Friend, come thou like a friend;
  And, whether bright thy face,
Or dim with clouds we cannot comprehend,
  We'll hold our patient hands, each in his place,
And trust thee to the end.
Knowing thou leadest onward to those spheres
Where there are neither days nor months nor years.

Ring Out, Wild Bells!

Alfred Tennyson

RING out, wild bells, to the wild sky,
  The flying cloud, the frosty light:
  The year is dying in the night;
Ring out, wild bells, and let him die.

Ring out the old, ring in the new,
  Ring, happy bells, across the snow;
  The year is going, let him go;
Ring out the false, ring in the true.

Ring out the grief that saps the mind,
   For those that here we see no more;
   Ring out the feud of rich and poor,
Ring in redress to all mankind.

Ring out a slowly dying cause,
   And ancient forms of party strife;
   Ring in the nobler modes of life,
With sweeter manners, purer laws.

Ring out the want, the care, the sin,
   The faithless coldness of the times;
   Ring out, ring out my mournful rhymes,
But ring the fuller minstrel in.

Ring out false pride in place and blood,
   The civic slander and the spite;
   Ring in the love of truth and right,
Ring in the common love of good.

Ring out old shapes of foul disease,
   Ring out the narrowing lust of gold;
   Ring out the thousand wars of old,
Ring in the thousand years of peace.

Ring in the valiant man and free,
   The larger heart, the kindlier hand;
   Ring out the darkness of the land,
Ring in the Christ that is to be.

Ring, Joyful Bells!

Violet Fuller

Ring, bells, from every lofty height!
An infant fair is born to-night;
Ring far and wide, ring full and clear,
To welcome in the glad New Year.
" The king is dead: long live the king!"
They said of old, and so we sing.
The Old Year has gone to his repose;
There let him rest beneath the snows.

Behind us, with the year that's gone,
Lie countless sins that we have done.
With joy we cast all care away,
And pass into another day.
New day, new life, whose noble deed
Will all our sinful years succeed.
A life of action, great and strong,
To cancel all we've done of wrong.

Ring, joyful bells! Our hearts beat high
With faith and hope, beyond the sky
Perchance the angels stand and wait
To catch the sound at heaven's gate.
And, echoing each silver tone,
Sing songs of praise around the throne.
Ring, happy bells! To us is given
Still longer to prepare for heaven.

On the Threshold

A. H. Baldwin

RING out, O bells! ring silver-sweet o'er hill and moor
and fell!
In mellow echoes let your chimes their hopeful story tell.
Ring out, ring out, all-jubilant, the joyous, glad refrain;
" A bright new year, a glad new year, hath come to us
again."

Ah! who can say how much of joy within it there may be
Stored up for us who listen now to your sweet melody?
Good-bye, Old Year! Tried, trusty friend, thy tale at last
is told.
O New Year! write thou thine for us in lines of brightest
gold.

The flowers of spring must bloom at last, when gone the
winter's snow;
God grant that, after sorrow past, we all some joy may
know.
Though tempest-tossed our bark awhile on Life's rough
waves may be,
There comes a day of calm at last, when we the haven see.

Then ring, ring on, O pealing bells! there's music in the
sound;
Ring on, ring on, and still ring on, and wake the echoes
round.
The while we wish, both for ourselves and all whom we
hold dear,
That God may gracious be to us in this, the bright New
Year!

Another Year

Thomas O'Hagan

ANOTHER year passed over — gone,
Hope beaming with the new;
Thus move we on — forever on,
The many and the few;
The many of our childhood's days,
Growing fewer, one by one,
Till death, in duel with each life
Proclaims the last is gone.

Another year — the buried past
Lies in its silent grave;
The stream of life flows ever on,
As wave leaps into wave;
Another year — ah! who can tell
What memories it may bring
Of lonely hearts and tearful eye,
And hope bereft of wing?

Another year — the curfew rings.
Fast cover up each coal;
The old year dies, the old year dies,
The bells its requiem toll;
A pilgrim year has reached its shrine,
The air with incense glows;
The spirit of another year
Comes forth from long repose!

Another year, with tears and joys,
To form an arch of love;
Another year to toil with hope,

And seek for rest above;
Another year winged on its way —
Eternity the goal;
Another year — peace in its train,
Peace to each parting soul!

Quotations for New Year's Day

From leafless hill and valley
But one refrain I hear;
" A merry, merry Christmas
And a glad New Year! "

— *George Cooper.*

" Brave and strong,
Bright as Phoenix, has the New Year,
Out of the ashes of the old, leaped forth
To rule the world in triumph."

— *Selected.*

Another year, with tears and joys,
To form the arch of love;
Another year to toil with hope,
And seek for rest above.

— *Thomas O'Hagan.*

"Next year, next year! "
Oh! why not now,
Delaying soul, *this* year
Keep word and vow?

— *Nora Perry.*

For what joy untold
Doth the New Year hold,
And what hopes within it sleep!

— *George Cooper.*

Press onward through each varying hour
Let no weak fears thy course delay.
Immortal being! feel thy power,
Pursue thy bright and endless way.

—*A. Norton.*

Ring out, ring out, all-jubilant, the joyous, glad refrain:
" A bright new year, a glad new year, hath come to us
again! "

—*A. H. Baldwin.*

" My seasons four shall bring
Their treasures: the winter's snows,
The autumn's stores, and the flowers of spring,
And the summer's perfect rose."

—*Celia Thaxter.*

The book of the New Year is opened,
Its pages are spotless and new;
And so, as each leaflet is turning,
Dear children, beware what you do.

—*Anonymous.*

O tell us, Year — we are fain to know —
What is thy charm that we hail thee so?

—*Margaret Sangster.*

For on the threshold, waiting, stands
The New Year's herald, Hope.

—*Eliza F. Moriarty.*

Ring in the love of truth and right;
Ring in the common love of good.

—*Alfred Tennyson.*

Why do we greet thee, O blithe New Year!
What are thy pledges of mirth and cheer?
Comest, knight-errant, the wrong to right?
Comest to scatter our gloom with light?

Wherefore the thrill, the sparkle and shine,
In heart and eyes at a word of thine?
                    — *Margaret E. Sangster.*

"Hold me in honor and greet me dear,
And sooth you'll find me a Happy New Year."
                    — *Margaret E. Sangster.*

HE held his place —
Held the long purpose like a growing tree —
Held on through blame and faltered not at praise.
And when he fell in whirlwind, he went down
As when a lordly cedar, green with boughs,
Goes down with a great shout upon the hills,
And leaves a lonesome place against the sky.

— Edwin Markham.

LINCOLN'S BIRTHDAY

February 12

Abraham Lincoln, who believed in a "government of the people, by the people, and for the people," was born February 12, 1809, near Hodgenville, Kentucky. He was elected president in 1861 and during his administration the Civil War was waged between the North and South. Under his careful guidance "with malice toward none, with charity for all," the Union was saved and the slaves set free. He was assassinated in Washington in April, 1865, a few days after the close of the war. His birthday has been made a legal holiday in twenty-six of the States and in Alaska and Porto Rico.

Abraham Lincoln

Samuel Valentine Cole

WHENCE came this man?   As if on the wings
  Of the winds of God that blew!
He moved, undaunted, mid captains and kings,
  And, not having learned, he knew!
Was he son of the soil, or child of the sky?
  Or, pray, was he both?   Ah me!
How little they dreamed, as the storm rolled nigh,
  What he was, and was to be!

When trembled the lamps of hope, or quite
  Blew out in that furious gale,
He drew his light from the Larger Light
  Above him that did not fail:
Heaven-led, all trials and perils among,
  As unto some splendid goal
He fared right onward, unflinching — this strong,
  God-gifted, heroic soul!

We know him now — how noble his part,
  And how clear was his vision then!
With the firmest hand and the kindliest heart
  Of them all — this master of men!
Of the pride of power or the lust of pelf,
  Oh, never a taint we find:
He lost himself in the larger self
  Of his country and all mankind.

There are those called great, or good, by right,
    But as long as the long roll is,
Not many the names, with the double light
    Of greatness and goodness, like his.
Thrice happy the nation that holds him dear
    Who never can wholly die,
Never cease to bestow of his counsel and cheer,
    As the perilous years go by!

For after the trumpets have ceased to blow,
    And the banners are folded away,
And the stress and the splendor forgotten, we know,
    Of a truth, in that judgment day,
That whatso'er else, in the Stream that rolls,
    May sink and be utterly gone,
The souls of the men who were true to their souls
    Forever go marching on!

There are those whose like, it was somehow planned,
    We never again shall see;
But I would to God there were more in the land
    As true and as simple as he,—
As he who walked in our common ways,
    With the seal of a king on his brow;
Who lived as a man among men his days,
    And belongs to the ages now!

O Captain! My Captain!

Walt Whitman

O CAPTAIN! my Captain! our fearful trip is done,
The ship has weather'd every rack, the prize we sought
is won,
The port is near, the bells I hear, the people all exulting,
While follow eyes the steady keel, the vessel grim and
daring;
But O heart! heart! heart!
O the bleeding drops of red,
Where on the deck my Captain lies,
Fallen cold and dead.

O Captain! my Captain! rise up and hear the bells;
Rise up — for you the flag is flung — for you the bugle
trills.
For you bouquets and ribbon'd wreaths — for you the
shores a-crowding,
For you they call, the swaying mass, their eager faces
turning;
Here, Captain! dear father!
This arm beneath your head!
It is some dream that on the deck,
You've fallen cold and dead.

My Captain does not answer, his lips are pale and still,
My father does not feel my arm, he has no pulse nor will,
The ship is anchor'd safe and sound, its voyage closed and
done,
From fearful trip the victor ship comes in with object
won;

Exult, O shores, and ring, O bells!
.But I with mournful tread,
   Walk the deck my Captain lies,
   Fallen cold and dead.

Our Martyr-Chief

James Russell Lowell

SUCH was he, our Martyr-Chief,
   Whom late the Nation he had led,
   With ashes on her head,
Wept with the passion of an angry grief:
Forgive me, if from present things I turn
To speak what in my heart will beat and burn,
And hang my wreath on his world-honored urn.
   Nature, they say, doth dote,
   And cannot make a man
   Save on some worn-out plan,
   Repeating us by rote;
For him her Old World moulds aside she threw,
   And, choosing sweet clay from the breast
   Of the unexhausted West,
With stuff untainted shaped a hero new,
Wise, steadfast in the strength of God, and true.
   How beautiful to see,
Once more a shepherd of mankind indeed,
Who loved his charge, but never loved to lead;
One whose meek flock the people joyed to be,
   Not lured by any cheat of birth,
   But by his clear-grained human worth,
And brave old wisdom of sincerity!
   They knew that outward grace is dust;
   They could not choose but trust

In the sure-footed mind's unfaltering skill,
    And supple-tempered will
That bent like perfect steel to spring again and thrust.
    His was no lonely mountain-peak of mind,
Thrusting to thin air o'er our cloudy bars,
    A sea-mark now, now lost in vapors blind;
    Broad prairie rather, genial, level-lined,
    Fruitful and friendly for all human kind,
Yet also nigh to heaven and loved of loftiest stars.

Great captains, with their guns and drums,
Disturb our judgment for the hour,
    But at last silence comes;
These all are gone, and standing like a tower,
    Our children shall behold his fame,
    The kindly-earnest, brave, foreseeing man,
Sagacious, patient, dreading praise, not blame,
New birth of our new soil, the first American.

By permission of and special arrangement with Houghton-
Mifflin Co.

Abraham Lincoln

Richard Henry Stoddard

THIS man whose homely face you look upon,
    Was one of nature's masterful, great men;
Born with strong arms, that unfought battles won;
    Direct of speech, and cunning with the pen.
Chosen for large designs, he had the art
    Of winning with his humor, and he went
Straight to his mark, which was the human heart;
    Wise, too, for what he could not break he bent.

Upon his back a more than Atlas-load,
  The burden of the Commonwealth, was laid;
He stooped, and rose up to it, though the road
  Shot suddenly downwards, not a whit dismayed.
Hold, warriors, councillors, kings! All now give place
To this dear benefactor of the race.

By permission of Charles Scribner's Sons.

Abraham Lincoln, the Master

Thomas Curtis Clark

WE need him now — his rugged faith that held
Fast to the rock of Truth through all the days
Of moil and strife, the sleepless nights; upheld
By very God was he — that God who stays
All hero-souls who will but trust in Him,
And trusting, labor as if God were not.
His eyes beheld the stars, clouds could not dim
Their glory; but his task was not forgot —
To keep his people one; to hold them true
To that fair dream their fathers willed to them —
Freedom for all; to spur them; to renew
Their hopes in bitter days; strife to condemn.
Such was his task, and well his work was done —
Who willed us greater tasks, when set his sun.

Lincoln

Henry Tyrrell

LINCOLN arose! the masterful, great man,
Girt with rude grandeur, quelling doubt and fear —
A more than king, yet in whose veins there ran
The red blood of the people, warm, sincere,
Blending of Puritan and Cavalier,
A will whose force stern warriors came to ask,
A heart that melted at a mother's tear —
These brought he to his his superhuman task;
Over a tragic soul he wore a comic mask.

He was the South's child more than of the North!
His soul was not compact of rock and snow,
But such as old Kentucky's soil gives forth —
The splendid race of giants that we know,
Firm unto friend, and loyal unto foe,
Such birthrights all environment forestall,
Resistlessly their tides of impulse flow.
This man who answered to his country's call
Was full of human faults, and nobler for them all.

He is a life, and not a legend, yet:
For thousands live who shook him by the hand,
Millions whose sympathies with his were set,
Whose hopes and griefs alike with his were grand,
Who deeply mourned his passing. They demand
Our homage to the greatest man they saw —
They, his familiars; and throughout our land
The years confirm them, over race and law:
Even of rancor now the voice is hush'd in awe.

Abraham Lincoln Walks at Midnight

Vachel Lindsay

It is portentous, and a thing of state
    That here at midnight, in our little town
A mourning figure walks, and will not rest,
    Near the old courthouse pacing up and down.

Or by his homestead, or in shadowed yards
    He lingers where his children used to play,
Or through the market, on the well-worn stones
    He stalks until the dawn-stars burn away.

A bronzed, lank man! His suit of ancient black,
    A famous high-top hat and plain worn shawl
Make him the quaint great figure that men love,
    The prairie lawyer, master of us all.

He cannot sleep upon his hillside now.
    He is among us;—as in times before!
And we who toss and lie awake for long
    Breathe deep, and start, to see him pass the door.

His head is bowed. He thinks on men and kings.
    Yea, when the sick world cries, how can he sleep?
Too many peasants fight, they know not why,
    Too many homesteads in black terror weep.

The sins of all the war-lords burn his heart.
    He sees the dreadnaughts scouring every main.
He carries on his shawl-wrapped shoulders now
    The bitterness. the folly and the pain.

Lincoln

Maurice Thompson

HE was the North, the South, the East, the West,
The thrall, the martyr, all of us in one;
There was no section that he held the best;
His love alone as impartial as the sun;
And so revenge appealed to him in vain,
He smiled at it, as at a thing forlorn,
And gently put it from him, rose and stood
    A moment's space in pain,
Remembering the prairies and the corn
And the glad voices of the field and wood.

And then when Peace set wing upon the wind
And northward flying fanned the clouds away,
He passed as martyrs pass. Ah, who shall find
The chord to sound the pathos of that day?
Mid-April blowing sweet across the land,
New bloom of freedom opening to the world,
Loud paeans of the homeward looking host,
    The salutations grand
From grimy guns, the tattered flags unfurled;
But he must sleep to all the glory lost!

Abraham Lincoln

Ralph Waldo Emerson

PRESIDENT Lincoln stood before us as a man of the people. He was thoroughly American, had never crossed the
sea, had never been spoiled by English insularity or
French dissipation; a quite native, aboriginal man, as an

acorn from an oak; no aping of foreigners, no frivolous accomplishments, Kentuckian born, working on a farm, a flatboatman, a captain in the Black Hawk war, a country lawyer, a representative in the rural Legislature of Illinois; on such modest foundations the broad structure of his fame was laid.

He offered no shining qualities at the first encounter; he did not offend by superiority. He had a face and manner which disarmed suspicion, which inspired confidence, which confirmed good-will. He was a man without vices. He had a strong sense of duty, which it was very easy for him to obey. Then, he had what farmers called a long head; was excellent in working out the sum for himself; in arguing his case and convincing you fairly and firmly. Then, it turned out that he was a great worker; had prodigious faculty of performance; worked easily. A good worker is so rare; everybody had some disabling quality. But this man was sound to the core, cheerful, persistent, all right for labor, and liked nothing so well.

Then, he had a vast good-nature, which made him tolerant and accessible to all; fair-minded, leaning to the claim of the petitioner; affable and not sensible to the affliction which the innumerable visits paid to him while President would have brought to any one else. And how this good-nature became a noble humanity, in many a tragic case which the events of the war brought to him, every one will remember; and with what increasing tenderness he dealt when a whole race was thrown on his compassion. The poor negro said of him, on an important occasion, " Massa Linkun am eberywhere."

From *Miscellanies.*

Lincoln's Gettysburg Address

FOURSCORE and seven years ago, our fathers brought forth upon this continent a new nation, conceived in liberty, and dedicated to the proposition that all men are created equal. Now we are engaged in a great civil war, testing whether that nation, or any nation so conceived and so dedicated, can long endure. We are met on a great battle-field of that war. We have come to dedicate a portion of that field as a final resting-place for those who here gave their lives that that nation might live. It is altogether fitting and proper that we should do this. But in a larger sense we cannot dedicate, we cannot consecrate, we cannot hallow this ground. The brave men living and dead, who struggled here, have consecrated it far above our power to add or detract. The world will little note nor long remember what we say here but it can never forget what they did here. It is for us, the living, rather to be dedicated here to the unfinished work which they who fought here have thus far so nobly advanced. It is rather for us to be here dedicated to the great task remaining before us, that from these honored dead we take increased devotion to that cause for which they here gave the last full measure of devotion; that we here highly resolve that these dead shall not have died in vain; that this nation, under God, shall have a new birth of freedom, and that government of the people, by the people, and for the people, shall not perish from the earth.

Words of Lincoln

LEARN the laws and obey them.

I am nothing, but truth is everything.

Killing the dog does not cure the bite.

Give us a little more light, and a little less noise.

It is not best to swap horses while crossing a stream.

He sticks through thick and thin — I admire such a man.

Success does not so much depend on external help as on self-reliance.

It is better only sometimes to be right than at all times to be wrong.

When you have an elephant on hand, and he wants to run away — better let him run.

Gold is good in its place; but living, brave, and patriotic men are better than gold.

My experience and observation have been that those who promise the most do the least.

The face of an old friend is like a ray of sunshine through dark and gloomy clouds.

I must stand with anybody that stands right; stand with him while he is right, and part with him when he goes wrong.

I am not bound to win, but I am bound to be true.

Quotations for Lincoln's Birthday

The Shepherd of the People! that old name that the best rulers ever craved. He fed us faithfully and truly. He spread before the whole land feasts of great duty and devotion and patriotism on which the land grew strong. He taught us the sacredness of government, the wickedness of treason.— *Phillips Brooks.*

> A power was his beyond the touch of art
> Or armed strength,— a pure and mighty heart.
> *— Richard W. Gilder.*

He has no parallel since Washington, and while our republic endures, he will live with him in the grateful hearts of his grateful countrymen.— *Schuyler Colfax.*

Lincoln was the purest, the most generous, the most magnanimous of men. He will hold a place in the world's history loftier than that of any king or conqueror. It is no wonder that the parliament of Europe, that the people throughout the civilized world, should everywhere speak of him with reverence; for his work was one of the greatest labors a human intellect ever sustained.— *John Sherman.*

He offered no shining qualities at the first encounter; he did not offend by superiority; he had a face and manner that disarmed suspicion, which inspired confidence, which confirmed good-will.— *Ralph Waldo Emerson.*

A man of great ability, pure patriotism, unselfish nature, full of forgiveness for his enemies.— *Ulysses S. Grant.*

The purity of his patriotism inspired him with the wisdom of a statesman and the courage of a martyr.— *Stanley Matthews.*

Such a life and character will be treasured forever as the sacred possession of the American people and of mankind. — *James A. Garfield.*

In Lincoln there was always some quality that fastened him to the people and taught them to keep time to the music of his heart.— *David Swing.*

A great man, tender of heart, strong of nerve, of boundless patience and broadest sympathy, with no motive apart from his country.— *Frederick Douglass.*

He has passed from our view. We shall not meet him again until he stands forth to answer to his name at the roll-call when the great of earth are summoned in the morning of the last great reveille. Till then, farewell, gentlest of spirits, noblest of all hearts ! The child's simplicity was mingled with the majestic grandeur of your nature. You have handed down unto a grateful people the richest legacy which man can leave to man — the memory of a good name — the inheritance of a great example.— *Horace Porter.*

Abraham Lincoln leaves for America's history and biography, so far, not only its most dramatic reminiscences — he leaves, in my opinion, the greatest, best, most characteristic, artistic, moral personality. Not but that he had faults, and showed them in the presidency; but honesty, goodness, shrewdness, conscience, and (a new virtue, unknown to other lands, and hardly yet known here, but the foundation of all, as the future will grandly develop), *Unionism,* in its truest and amplest sense, formed the hardpan of his character. These he sealed with his life. The tragic splendor of his death, purging, illuminating all, throws round his head an aureole that will remain and will grow brighter through time, while history lives, and love of country lasts.— *Walt Whitman.*

No higher compliment was ever paid to a nation than the simple confidence, the fireside plainness, with which Mr. Lincoln always addressed himself to the reason of the American people. This was, indeed, a true democrat, who grounded himself on the assumption that a democracy can think.— *James Russell Lowell.*

A civilian during time of the most captivating, military achievement, awkward, with no skill in the lower technicalities of manners, he left behind him a fame beyond that of any conqueror, the memory of a grace higher than that of outward person, and of gentlemanliness deeper than mere breeding.— *James Russell Lowell.*

I doubt if history affords any example of a life so early, so deeply and so permanently influenced by a single political truth, as was Abraham Lincoln's by the central doctrine of the Declaration — the liberty and equality of men. Long before his fame had become national he said, " That is the electric cord in the Declaration, that links the hearts of patriotic and liberty-loving men together, and that will link such hearts as long as the love of freedom exists in the minds of men throughout the world.— *James A. Garfield.*

To him was given the duty and responsibility of making that great classic of liberty, the Declaration of Independence, no longer an empty promise, but a glorious fulfillment.— *William McKinley.*

Lincoln thought always of mankind as well as of his own country, and served human nature itself; he finished a work which all time cannot overthrow.— *George Bancroft.*

It is the glory of Lincoln that, having almost absolute power, he never abused it, except on the side of mercy.

Wealth could not purchase, power could not awe, this divine, this loving man.

He knew no fear except the fear of doing wrong. Hating slavery, pitying the master — seeking to conquer, not persons, but prejudices — he was the embodiment of self-denial, the courage, the hope and the nobility of a Nation.

He spoke not to inflame, not to upbraid, but to convince. He raised his hands, not to strike, but in benediction.

He loved to see the pearls of joy on the cheeks of a wife whose husband he had rescued from death.

Lincoln was the grandest figure of the greatest Civil War.

He is the gentlest memory of our world.— *Robert G. Ingersoll.*

A man of great ability, pure patriotism, unselfish nature, full of forgiveness to his enemies, bearing malice toward none, he proved to be the man of all others for the struggle through which the nation had to pass to place itself among the greatest in the family of nations. His fame will grow brighter as time passes and his great work is better understood.— *U. S. Grant.*

Thy task is done — the bond are free;
 We bear thee to an honored grave,
Whose noblest monuments shall be
 The broken fetters of the slave.

Pure was thy life; its bloody close
 Hath placed thee with the sons of light,
Among the noblest host of those
 Who perished in the cause of right.
 — *William Cullen Bryant.*

Our children shall behold his fame,
 The kindly-earnest, brave fore-seeing man,
Sagacious, patient, dreading praise, not blame,
 New birth of our new soil, the First American.
 — *James Russell Lowell.*

Human glory is often fickle as the winds, and transient as a summer day; but Abraham Lincoln's place in history is assured. He stands forth on the page of history, unique in his character, and majestic in his individuality. He was of the people and for the people.— *Bishop John P. Newman.*

Not in vain has Lincoln lived, for he has helped to make this republic an example of justice, with no caste but the caste of humanity.— *George Bancroft.*

He was the greatest President in American History, because in a time of revolution he grasped the purpose of the American people and embodied them in an act of justice and humanity which was in the highest sense the act of the American Republic.— *Lyman Abbott.*

> Grave Lincoln came, strong-handed from afar,—
> The mighty Homer of the lyre of war!
> 'Twas he who bade the raging tempest cease,
> Wrenched from his strings the harmony of peace,
> Muted the strings that made the discord — Wrong,
> And gave his spirit up in thund'rous song.
> Oh, mighty Master of the mighty lyre!
> Earth heard and trembled at thy strains of fire:
> Earth learned of thee what Heav'n already knew,
> And wrote thee down among the treasured few!
> — *Paul Laurence Dunbar.*

From humble parentage and poverty, old Nature reared him,
And the world beheld her ablest, noblest man;
Few were his joys, many and terrible his trials,
But grandly he met them as only truly great souls can!
Our Nation's Martyr, pure, honest, patient, tender,—
Thou who didst suffer agony e'en for the slave,—
Our flag's defender, our brave, immortal teacher!
I lay this humble tribute on thy honored grave.
— *Paul DeVere.*

And thus there is a constant pledge that the cherishing of Lincoln's memory has become, indeed, a portion of our national heritage.— *M. A. DeWolf Howe.*

In his mentality, he shone in judgment, common sense, consistency, persistence, and in knowledge of men. In his words, he was candid and frank, but accurate and concise, speaking sturdy Anglo-Saxon unadorned, powerful in its simplicity and the subdued enthusiasm of earnest thought. In his sentiments, he was kind and patient and brave. No leader ever more completely combined in his personality the graces of gentleness with rugged determination. In his morals, Truth was his star; Honesty the vital air of his living. In his religion, he was faithful as a giant; Providence was his stay; he walked with God.— *Luther Laflin Mills.*

ALONE in its grandeur stands forth the character of Washington in history; alone like some peak that has no fellow in the mountain-range of greatness.

Statesman, soldier, patriot, sage, achiever and preserver of liberty, the first of men, founder and saviour of his country, father of his people — this is he, solitary and unapproachable in his grandeur.— *John W. Daniel.*

WASHINGTON'S BIRTHDAY

February 22

George Washington was born on February 22, 1732, near Bridges Creek, Westmoreland Co., Virginia. His birthday, in the process of time, has been made a legal holiday by every State, Territory and possession of the United States. It was first celebrated by Count de Rochambeau (the French General who came to the aid of our country during the Revolutionary War) at Newport, R. I., in 1781. It was celebrated in New York City, in the first popular celebration of the day, in 1784, less than three months after the departure of the British.

Washington's Birthday

Margaret E. Sangster

'Tis splendid to live so grandly
   That, long after you are gone,
The things you did are remembered,
   And recounted under the sun;
To live so bravely and purely
   That a nation stops on its way,
And once a year, with banner and drum,
   Keeps its thought of your natal day.

'Tis splendid to have a record
   So white and free from stain
That, held to the light, it shows no blot,
   Though tested and tried amain;
That age to age forever
   Repeats its story of love,
And your birthday lives in a nation's heart,
   All other days above.

And this is Washington's glory,
   A steadfast soul and true,
Who stood for his country's honor
   When his country's days were few.
And now, when its days are many,
   And its flag of stars is flung
To the breeze in defiant challenge,
   His name is on every tongue.

Yes, it's splendid to live so bravely,
　　To be so great and strong,
That your memory is ever a tocsin
　　To rally the foes of wrong;
To live so proudly and purely
　　That your people pause in their way,
And year by year, with banner and drum,
　　Keep the thought of your natal day.

Washington

Anonymous

WE are met to testify our regard for him whose name is intimately blended with whatever belongs most essentially to the prosperity, the liberty, the free institutions, and the renown of our country. That name was a power to rally a nation in the hour of thick-thronging public disasters and calamities; that name shone amid the storm of war, a beacon light to cheer and guide the country's friends; its flame, too, like a meteor, to repel her foes. That name in the days of peace was a loadstone, attracting to itself a whole people's confidence, a whole people's love, and the whole world's respect; that name, descending with all time, spread over the whole earth, and uttered in all the languages belonging to the tribes and races of men, will forever be pronounced with affectionate gratitude by every one in whose breast there shall arise an aspiration for human rights and human liberty.

Washington stands at the commencement of a new era, as well as at the head of the New World. A century from the birth of Washington has changed the world. The country of Washington has been wrought, and

Washington himself a principal agent by which it has been accomplished. His age and his country are equally full of wonders, and of both he is the chief.

It is the spirit of human freedom, the new elevation of individual man, in his moral, social, and political character, leading the whole long train of other improvements, which has most remarkably distinguished the era. Society has assumed a new character; it has raised itself from beneath governments to a participation in governments; it has mixed moral and political objects with the daily pursuits of individual men, and, with a freedom and strength before altogether unknown, it has applied to these objects the whole power of the human understanding. It has been the era, in short, when the social principle has triumphed over the feudal principle; when society has maintained its rights against military power, and established on foundations never hereafter to be shaken its competency to govern itself.

Washington's Birthday

Oliver Wendell Holmes

WELCOME to the day returning,
  Dearer still as ages flow,
While the torch of Faith is burning,
  Long as Freedom's altars glow!
See the hero whom it gave us
  Slumbering on a mother's breast;
For the arm he stretched to save us,
  Be its morn forever blest!

Hear the tale of youthful glory,
  While of Britain's rescued band

Friend and foe repeat the story,
   Spread his fame o'er sea and land,
Where the red cross, proudly streaming,
   Flaps above the frigate's deck,
Where the golden lilies, gleaming,
   Star the watch-towers of Quebec.

Look! The shadow on the dial
   Marks the hour of deadlier strife;
Days of terror, years of trial,
   Scourge a nation into life.
Lo, the youth, becomes her leader!
   All her baffled tyrants yield;
Through his arms the Lord hath freed her;
   Crown him on the tented field!

Vain is Empire's mad temptation!
   Not for him an earthly crown!
He whose sword hath freed a nation
   Strikes the offered sceptre down.
See the throneless Conqueror seated,
   Ruler by a people's choice;
See the Patriot's task completed;
   Hear the Father's dying voice!

" By the name that you inherit,
   By the sufferings you recall,
Cherish the fraternal spirit;
   Love your country first of all!
Listen not to idle questions
   If its bands may be untied;
Doubt the patriot whose suggestions
   Strive a nation to divide! "

Father! We, whose ears have tingled
  With the discord-notes of shame,—
We, whose sires their blood have mingled
  In the battle's thunder-flame,—
Gathering, while this holy morning
Lights the land from sea to sea,
Hear thy counsel, heed thy warning;
  Trust us, while we honor thee!

Washington

Under the Old Elm

SOLDIER and statesman, rarest unison;
High-poised example of great duties done
Simply as breathing, a world's honors worn
As life's indifferent gifts to all men born;
Dumb for himself, unless it were to God,
But for his barefoot soldiers eloquent,
Tramping the snow to coral where they trod,
Held by his awe in hollow-eyed content;
Modest, yet firm as Nature's self; unblamed
Save by the men his nobler temper shamed;
Never seduced through show of present good
By other than unsetting lights to steer
New-trimmed in Heaven, nor than his steadfast mood
More steadfast, far from rashness as from fear;
Rigid, but with himself first, grasping still
In swerveless poise the wave-beat helm of will;
Not honored then or now because he wooed
The popular voice, but that he still withstood;
Broad-minded, higher-souled, there is but one
Who was all this and ours, and all men's,— WASHING-
  TON.

The Star in the West

Eliza Cook

THERE'S a star in the West, that shall never go down,
　Till the records of valor decay;
We must worship its light, though it is not our own,
　For liberty burst in its ray.
Shall the name of a Washington ever be heard
　By a freeman, and thrill not his breast?
Is there one out of bondage, that hails not the word
　As the Bethlehem star of the West?

" War, war to the knife! be enthralled or ye die,"
　Was the echo that woke in his land;
But it was not *his* voice that prompted the cry,
　Nor *his* madness that kindled the brand.
He raised not his arm, he defied not his foes,
　While a leaf of the olive remained;
Till goaded with insult, his spirit arose
　Like a long-baited lion unchained.

He struck with firm courage the blow of the brave,
　But sighed o'er the carnage that spread;
He indignantly trampled the yoke of the slave,
　But wept for the thousands that bled.
Though he threw back the fetters, and headed the strife,
　Till man's charter was fairly restored;
Yet he prayed for the moment when freedom and life
　Would no longer be pressed by the sword.

Oh! his laurels were pure, and his patriotic-name
　In the page of the future shall dwell,
And be seen in all annals, the foremost in fame,
　By the side of a HOFER and TELL,

Revile not my song, for the wise and the good
  Among Britons have nobly confessed,
That his was the glory, and ours was the blood
  Of the deeply-stained field of the West.

Our Washington

Eliza W. Durbin

O son of Virginia, thy mem'ry divine
Forever will halo this country of thine.
Not hero alone in the battle's wild strife,
But hero in ev'ry detail of thy life.
So noble, unselfish, heroic, and true,
A God-given gift to thy country were you;
And lovingly, tenderly guarding thy shrine,
Columbia points proudly, and says: "He is mine."

Thy courage upheld us, thy judgment sustained,
Thy spirit stood proof when discouragement reigned,
Thy justice unerring all bias withstood,
Thy thought never self, but thy loved country's good.
And thy country will never, till time is no more,
Cease to cherish the sleeper on yon river's shore;
And ev'ry fair daughter and ev'ry brave son
She will tell of the greatness of her Washington.

O hero immortal! O spirit divine!
What glory eternal, what homage is thine!
Forever increasing will be thy renown,
With the stars of Columbia that gleam in thy crown.
The God who guards liberty gave thee to earth,
Forever we'll honor thy heaven-sent birth.
E'en heaven itself has one gladness the more
That our hands shall clasp thine on eternity's shore.

Then sleep, sweetly sleep, by the river's calm run;
Thy fame will live on in the land thou hast won;
To Potomac's soft music then slumber serene,
The spirit of freedom will keep the spot green;
And so long as time echoes the hour of thy birth,
We will pay loving tribute and praise to thy worth,
And pledge to keep spotless the freedom you gave,
And the land that is hallowed by Washington's grave.

Crown Our Washington

Hezekiah Butterworth

ARISE — 'Tis the day of our Washington's glory,
   The garlands uplift for our liberties won;
Forever let Youth tell the patriot's story,
     Whose sword swept for freedom the fields of the sun!
       Not with gold, nor with gems,
       But with evergreens vernal,
And the banners of stars that the continent span,
   Crown, crown we the chief of the heroes eternal,
Who lifted his sword for the birthright of man!

He gave us a nation; to make it immortal
   He laid down for Freedom the sword that he drew,
And his faith leads us on through the uplifting portal
     Of the glories of peace and our destinies new.
       Not with gold, nor with gems,
       But with evergreens vernal,
And the flags that the nations of liberty span,
   Crown, crown him the chief of the heroes eternal,
Who laid down his sword for the birthright of man!

Lead, Face of the Future, serene in thy beauty,
   Till o'er the dead heroes the peace star shall gleam,

Till Right shall be Might in the counsels of duty,
  And the service of man be life's glory supreme.
    Not with gold, nor with gems,
    But with evergreens vernal,
And the flags that the nations in brotherhood span,
  Crown, crown we the chief of the heroes eternal,
Whose honor was gained by his service to man!

O Spirit of Liberty, sweet are thy numbers!
  The winds to thy banners their tribute shall bring
While rolls the Potomac where Washington slumbers,
  And his natal day comes with the angels of spring.
    We follow thy counsels,
    O hero eternal!
To highest achievement the school leads the van,
  And, crowning thy brow with the evergreen vernal,
We pledge thee our all to the service of man!

The Glory of Washington

Timothy Dwight

To Americans the name of Washington will be forever
dear,— a savor of sweet incense, descending to every
succeeding generation. The things which he has done
are too great, too interesting, ever to be forgotten. Every
object which we see, every employment in which we are
engaged, every comfort which we enjoy, reminds us
daily of his character.

Every ship bears the fruit of his labors on its wings
and exultingly spreads its streamers to his honor. The
student meets him in the still and peaceful walk; the
traveler sees him in all the smiling and prosperous scenes
of his journey; and our whole country, in her thrift,

order. safety, and morals, bears inscribed in sunbeams,
on all her hills and plains, the name and glory of Washington.

George Washington

Anonymous

ONLY a baby, fair and small,
　Like many another baby son,
Whose smiles and tears come swift at call;
Who ate, and slept, and grew, that's all —
　The infant Washington.

Only a boy, like other boys,
　With tasks and studies, sports and fun;
Fond of his books and games and toys;
Living his childish griefs and joys —
　The little Washington.

Only a lad, awkward and shy,
　Skilled in handling a horse or gun;
Mastering knowledge that, by and by,
Should aid him in duties great and high —
　The youthful Washington.

Only a man of finest bent,
　Hero of battles fought and won;
Surveyor, General, President,
Who served his country, and died content —
　The patriot Washington.

Only — ah! what was the secret, then,
　Of his being America's honored son?
Why was he famed above other men?
His name upon every tongue and pen —
　The illustrious Washington.

A mighty brain, a will to endure,
  Passions subdued, a slave to none,
A heart that was brave and strong and sure,
A soul that was noble and great and pure,
A faith in God that was held secure —
  This was George Washington.

United States as an Independent Power

George Washington

THERE are four things which I humbly conceive are essential to the well-being — I may even venture to say, to the existence of the United States, as an independent power.

First; An indissoluble Union of the States under one Federal head.

Second; A sacred regard to public justice.

Third; The adoption of a proper peace establishment.

Fourth; The prevalence of the pacific and friendly disposition among the people of the United States which will induce them to forget their local prejudices and politics; to make those mutual concessions which are requisite to the general prosperity; and in some instances, — to sacrifice their individual advantages to the interest of the community.

These are the pillars on which the glorious fabric of our independence and national character must be supported. Liberty is the basis. And whoever would dare to sap the foundation, or overturn the structure, under whatever specious pretext he may attempt it will merit the bitterest execration and the severest punishment which can be inflicted by his injured country.

Washington's Address to His Troops

George Washington

THE time is now near at hand which must probably determine whether Americans are to be freemen or slaves; whether they are to have any property they can call their own; whether their houses and farms are to be pillaged and destroyed, and themselves consigned to a state of wretchedness, from which no human efforts will deliver them. The fate of unborn millions will now depend, under God, on the courage and conduct of this army. Our cruel and unrelenting enemy leaves us only the choice of a brave resistance, or the most abject submission. We have, therefore, to resolve to conquer or to die.

Our own, our country's honor, calls upon us for a vigorous and manly exertion; and if we now shamefully fail, we shall become infamous to the whole world. Let us then rely on the goodness of our cause, and the aid of the Supreme Being, in whose hands victory is, to animate and encourage us to great and noble actions. The eyes of all our countrymen are now upon us, and we shall have their blessings and praises, if happily we are the instruments of saving them from the tyranny meditated against them. Let us animate and encourage each other, and show the whole world that a freeman contending for liberty on his own ground is superior to any slavish mercenary on earth.

Liberty, property, life, and honor are all at stake; upon your courage and conduct rest the hopes of our bleeding and insulted country; our wives, children, and parents expect safety from us, only; and they have every reason to believe that Heaven will crown with success so just a cause.

The enemy will endeavor to intimidate by show and appearance; but, remember, they have been repulsed on various occasions by a few brave Americans. Their cause is bad — their men are conscious of it; and, if opposed with firmness and coolness on their first onset, with our advantage of works, and knowledge of the ground, the victory is most assuredly ours. Every good soldier will be silent and attentive — wait for orders, and reserve his fire until he is sure of doing execution.

Some Maxims of Washington

Think before you speak.

Let your recreations be manful, not sinful.

Speak no evil of the absent, for it is unjust.

Let your conversation be without malice or envy.

Detract not from others, but neither be excessive in commending.

Let your discourse with men of business be short and comprehensive.

Be not hasty to believe flying reports to the disparagement of any one.

Show not yourself glad at the misfortune of another, though he were your enemy.

Undertake not what you cannot perform, but be careful to keep your promise.

Associate yourself with men of good quality if you esteem your reputation.

If a man does all he can, though he succeeds not well, blame not him that did it.

Labor to keep alive in your breast that little spark of celestial fire called conscience.

Washington's Rules of Conduct

When we understand something of the greatness of Washington, it is certainly a matter of interest to discover the rules by which he guided his life. The following rules should be studied by every school boy and girl, with the idea of discovering the extent to which they will guide one to succeed in life.

1. Reproach none for the infirmities of nature, nor delight to put them that have in mind thereof.
2. Do not express joy before one sick or in pain; for that contrary passion will aggravate his misery.
3. Every action in company ought to be with some sign of respect to those present.
4. In the presence of others, sing not to yourself with a humming noise, nor drum with your fingers or feet.
5. Sleep not when others speak; sit not when others stand; speak not when you should hold your peace; walk not when others stop.
6. Turn not your back to others, especially in speaking; jog not the table or desk on which another reads or writes; lean not on any one.
7. Read no letters, books, or papers in company; but when there is a necessity for doing it, you must ask leave. Come not near the books or writings of any one so as to read them, unless desired, nor give your opinion of them unasked; also, look not nigh when another is writing a letter.
8. Let your countenance be pleasant, but in serious matters somewhat grave.

9. Show not yourself glad at the misfortune of another, though he were your enemy.

10. Run not in the streets; neither go too slowly, nor with mouth open. Go not shaking your arms, stamping or shuffling; nor pull up your stocking in the street. Walk not upon the toes, nor in a dancing or skipping manner, nor yet with measured steps. Strike not the heels together, nor stoop when there is no occasion.

11. Eat not in the streets, nor in the house out of season.

12. While you are talking, point not with your finger at him of whom you discourse, nor approach too near him to whom you talk, especially to his face.

13. In writing or speaking, give to every person his due title, according to his degree and the custom of the place.

14. Take all admonitions thankfully, in what time or place soever given; but afterwards, not being culpable, take a time and place convenient to let him know it that gave them.

15. Drink not, nor talk with your mouth full; neither gaze about you while drinking.

16. Use no reproachable language against any one; neither curse nor revile.

17. If you cough, sneeze, sigh, or yawn, do it not loud, but privately: and speak not in your yawning, but put your handkerchief, or hand, before your face, and turn aside.

18. When you sit down, keep your feet firm and even, without putting one on the other, or crossing them.

19. In your apparel be modest, and endeavor to accommodate nature, rather than to procure admiration; keep to the fashion of your equals, such as are civil and orderly, with respect to times and places.

20. Play not the peacock, looking everywhere about you to see if you be well decked, if your shoes fit well, if your stockings fit neatly, and clothes handsomely.

21. Speak not of doleful things in time of mirth, nor at the table; speak not of melancholy things as death and wounds, and if others mention them change, if you can. the discourse. Tell not your dreams but to your intimate friend.

22. Speak not injurious words, neither in jest nor earnest; scoff at none, although they give occasion.

23. Be not forward, but friendly and courteous; the first to salute, hear and answer; and. be not pensive when it is time to converse.

24. Go not thither where you know not whether you shall be welcome or not. Give not advice without being asked, and when desired, do it briefly.

25. Gaze not on the marks or blemishes of others, and ask not how they came. What you may speak in secret to your friend, deliver not before others.

26. Think before you speak; pronounce not imperfectly, nor bring out your words too hastily, but orderly and distinctly.

27. When another speaks, be attentive yourself, and disturb not the audience. If any hesitate in his words, help him not, nor prompt him without being desired; interrupt him not, nor answer him till his speech be ended.

28. Be not apt to relate news if you know not the truth thereof. In discoursing of things you have heard, name not your author always. A secret discover not.

29. Be not curious to know the affairs of the others, neither approach to those that speak in private.

Quotations for Washington's Birthday

The birthday of the Father of his Country! "May it ever be freshly remembered by American hearts! May it ever reawaken in them a filial veneration for his memory; ever rekindle the fires of patriotic regard for the country which he loved so well, to which he gave his youthful vigor and his youthful energy; to which he devoted his life in the maturity of his powers, in the field; to which again he offered the counsels of his wisdom and his experience as president of the convention that framed our Constitution, which he guided and directed while in the chair of state, and for which the last prayer of his earthly supplication was offered up, when it came the moment for him so well, and so grandly, and so calmly, to die. He was the first man of the time in which he grew. His memory is first and most sacred in our love, and ever hereafter, till the last drop of blood shall freeze in the last American heart, his name shall be a spell of power and of might.—*Anonymous.*

The commemoration of any one great event in the life of Washington and of the United States is well, but it is nothing compared with the incessant memorial of him which the schools and colleges of the country maintain from generation to generation. What a reward was Washington's! What an influence was his and will be. One mind and will transfused by sympathetic instruction into millions; one life pattern for all public men, teaching what greatness is and what the pathway to undying fame! — *Charles W. Eliot.*

> The century just passed away,
> Has felt the impress of thy sway,
> While youthful hearts have stronger grown
> And made thy patriot zeal their own.
> In marble hall or lowly cot,
> Thy name hath never been forgot,
> The world itself is richer, far,

For the clear shining of a star.
And loyal hearts in years to run
Shall turn to thee, O Washington.
                    — *Mary Wingate.*

Washington's is the mightiest name of earth — long since mightiest in the cause of civil liberty; still mightiest in moral reformation. On that name no eulogy is expected. It cannot be. To add brightness to the sun, or glory to the name of Washington, is alike impossible. Let none attempt it. In solemn awe pronounce the name, and in its naked deathless splendor leave it shining on.— *Abraham Lincoln.*

His example is complete, and it will teach wisdom and virtue to magistrates, citizens and men, not only in the present age, but in future generations, as long as our history shall be read.— *John Adams.*

Where may the wearied eye repose
    When gazing on the great,
Where neither guilty glory glows
    Nor despicable state?
Yes,— one, the first, the last, the best,
The Cincinnatus of the West,
    Whom envy dared not hate,
Bequeathed the name of Washington
To make men blush there was but one.
                    — *Lord Byron.*

Let him who looks for a monument to Washington look around the United States. Your freedom, your independence, your national power, your prosperity, and your prodigious growth are a monument to him.— *Louis Kossuth.*

The form of Washington stands apart from every other in history, shining with a truer lustre and a more benignant glory. With us his memory remains a national property, where all sympathies meet in unison. Under all dissensions and amid all storms of party, his precepts and examples speak to us from the grave with a paternal appeal; and his name — by all revered — forms a universal tie of brother-hood,— a watchword of our Union.— *John Fiske.*

When the storm of battle blows darkest and rages highest, the memory of Washington shall nerve every American arm, and cheer every American heart.— *Rufus Choate.*

The Republic may perish, the wide arch of our Union may fall; star by star its glories may expire; stone after stone its columns and its capitol may moulder and crumble; all other names which adorn its annals may be forgotten; but as long as human hearts shall anywhere pant, or human tongue shall anywhere plead, for a sure, rational, constitu-tional liberty, those hearts shall enshrine the memory and those tongues shall prolong the fame of George Washington. — *R. C. Winthrop, at the laying of the corner-stone of the Washington monument.*

Marble columns may moulder in the dust, and time erase all impress from the crumbling stone, but his fame arose with American liberty, and with American liberty alone can perish.— *Daniel Webster.*

Eternity alone can reveal to the human race its debt of gratitude to the peerless and immortal name of Washington. — *James A. Garfield.*

ARBOR DAY AND BIRD DAY

April

It is not long since some of our treeless Western states, desiring to promote the culture of trees, appointed a day early in spring for popular tree planting. The time of the observance of Arbor day varies greatly in different states, being determined somewhat by climatic conditions. In many states it is combined with Bird Day. Ohio was the first state to advance this movement of spring planting by the institution of an arbor day to be celebrated and observed in the schools. This was in 1883. The other states, which have all suffered more or less wanton destruction of their primeval forests, soon joined the movement.

The Tree

Jones Very

I LOVE thee when thy swelling buds appear,
    And one by one their tender leaves unfold,
As if they knew that warmer suns were near,
    Nor longer sought to hide from winter's cold;
And when with darker growth thy leaves are seen
    To veil from view the early robin's nest,
I love to lie beneath thy waving screen,
    With limbs by summer's heat and toil oppressed;
And when the autumn winds have stripped thee bare,
    And round thee lies the smooth, untrodden snow,
When naught is thine that made thee once so fair,
    I love to watch thy shadowy form below,
And through thy leafless arms to look above
    On stars that brighter beam when most we need their
        love.

Spring Is Coming

Anonymous

I AM coming, little maiden!
With the pleasant sunshine laden,
With the honey for the bee,
With the blossoms for the tree,
With the flower, and with the leaf —
Till I come the time is brief.

I am coming! I am coming!
Hark! the little bee is humming;

See! the lark is soaring high
In the bright and sunny sky;
And the gnats are on the wing,
Wheeling round in airy ring.
See! the yellow catkins cover
All the slender willows over;
And on banks of mossy green
Starlike primroses are seen,
And their clustering leaves below,
White and purple violets blow.

Hark! the new-born lambs are bleating
And the cawing rooks are meeting
In the elms — a noisy crowd!
All the birds are singing loud;
And the first white butterfly
In the sunshine dances by.

The Coming of Spring

Selected

THE Birds are coming home soon;
  I look for them every day;
I listen to catch the first wild strain,
  For they must be singing by May.

The bluebird, he'll come first, you know,
  Like a violet that has taken wings;
And the red-breast trills while his nest he builds,
  I can hum the song that he sings.

And the crocus and wind-flower are coming, too;
  They're already upon the way;

When the sun warms the brown earth through and
        through,
    I shall look for them any day.

Then be patient, and wait a little, my dear;
    " They're coming," the winds repeat;
" We're coming! we're coming! " I'm sure I hear,
    From the grass blades that grow at my feet.

Talking In Their Sleep

Edith M. Thomas

    " You think I am dead,"
        The apple tree said,
" Because I have never a leaf to show —
        Because I stoop
        And my branches droop,
    And the dull gray mosses over me grow!
    But I'm still alive in trunk and shoot;
        The buds of next May
        I fold away,—
    But I pity the withered grass at my feet."

    " You think I am dead,"
        The quick grass said,
" Because I have parted with stem and blade!
        Because under the ground
        I am safe and sound
    With the snow's thick blanket over me laid.
    I'm all alive and ready to shoot,
        Should the spring of the year
        Come dancing here,—
    But I pity the flowers without branch or root."

" You think I am dead,"
A soft voice said,
" Because not a branch or root I own!
I never have died
But close I hide
In a plumy seed that the wind has sown.
Patiently I wait through the long winter hours;
You will see me again —
I shall laugh at you then,
Out of the eyes of a hundred flowers."

In April

Emily Gail Arnold

THE air is soft and balmy,
  The grass is growing green,
The maple buds are swelling,
  Till their tender threads are seen.
The brown brook chatters gayly
  Its rippling course along,
And hark! — from distant tree-top
  I hear the bluebird's song.

O joyous, gladsome carol,
  Exultant, fearless, true!
There is hidden a heavenly message
  'Neath that coat of heavenly blue.
My heart thrills as I listen;
  God's love is sure and strong.
Thank Him for life's awakening!
  Praise for the bluebird's song!

After the winter, springtime,
  The sunshine follows rain;

Tho' grief and sorrow chill us,
　　The heart grows warm again.
From earth to His glad heaven
　　God will His loved ones bring;
Still, after the frosts and snowdrifts,
　　We hear the bluebirds sing.

Waiting To Grow

Anonymous

LITTLE white snow-drops just waking up,
Violet, daisy and sweet buttercup;
Think of the flowers that are under the snow,
　　　　Waiting to grow!

And think of what hosts of queer little seeds
Of flowers and mosses, of fern and of weeds,
Are under the leaves and under the snow
　　　　Waiting to grow!

Think of the roots getting ready to sprout,
Reaching their slender brown fingers about
Under the ice and the leaves and the snow
　　　　Waiting to grow!

Only a month or a few weeks more,
Will they have to wait behind that door,
Listen and watch and wait below,
　　　　Waiting to grow!

Nothing so small, and hidden so well,
That God will not find it, and presently tell
His sun where to shine, and His rain where to go,
　　　　Helping them grow!

All Things Beautiful

John Keble

ALL things bright and beautiful,
  All creatures great and small,
All things wise and wonderful —
  The Lord God made them all.

Each little flower that opens,
  Each little bird that sings —
He made their glowing colors,
  He made their tiny wings.

The purple-headed mountain,
  The river running by,
The morning and the sunset
  That lighteth up the sky;

The tall trees in the greenwood,
  The pleasant summer sun,
The ripe fruits in the garden —
  He made them every one.

He gave us eyes to see them,
  And lips, that we might tell
How great is God Almighty,
  Who doeth all things well.

The Bluebird

Eben Eugene Rexford

LISTEN a moment, I pray you; what was that sound that
    I heard?
Wind in the budding branches, the ripple of brooks, or a
    bird?
Hear it again, above us! and see a flutter of wings!
The bluebird knows it is April, and soars toward the sun
    and sings.

Never the song of the robin could make my heart so glad;
When I hear the bluebird singing in spring, I forget to
    be sad.
Hear it! a ripple of music! sunshine changed into song!
It sets me thinking of summer when the days and their
    dreams are long.

Winged lute that we called a bluebird, you blend in a
    silver strain
The sound of the laughing water, the patter of spring's
    sweet rain.
The voice of the winds, the sunshine, and fragrance of
    blossoming things,
Ah! you are an April poem, that God has dowered with
    wings!

A Bird's Nest

Florence Percy

OVER my shaded doorway,
Two little brown-winged birds
Have chosen to fashion their dwelling,
And utter their loving words.
All day they are going and coming
On errands frequent and fleet,
And warbling over and over —
" Sweetest, sweet, sweet, O sweet! "

Their necks are changeful and shining,
Their eyes are like living gems,
And all day long they are busy,
Gathering straws and stems,
Lint and feathers and grasses;
And half forgetting to eat;
Yet never failing to warble,
" Sweetest, sweet, sweet, O sweet! "

I scatter crumbs on the doorsteps,
And fling them some flossy threads;
They fearlessly gather my bounty,
And turn up their graceful heads,
And chatter, and dance, and flutter,
And scrape their tiny feet,
Telling me, over and over,
" Sweetest, sweet, sweet, O sweet! "

What if the sky is clouded?
What if the rain comes down?
They are all dressed to meet it,

In waterproof suits of brown.
They never mope nor languish
Nor murmur at storm or heat,
But say,— whatever the weather,—
" Sweetest, sweet, sweet, O sweet!"

Always merry and busy,—
Dear little brown-winged birds,
Teach me the happy magic
Hidden in these soft words,
Which always, in shine or shadow,
So lovingly you repeat
Over, and over, and over,
" Sweetest, sweet, sweet, O sweet!"

The Brown Thrush

Lucy Larcom

THERE's a merry brown thrush sitting up in a tree —
    " He's singing to me; he's singing to me!"
And what does he say, little girl, little boy?
    " ' Oh, the world's running over with joy!
        Don't you hear? Don't you see?
        Hush! Look! In my tree,
I'm as happy as happy can be!' "

And the brown thrush keeps singing —" A nest do
            you see
    And five eggs, hid by me in the juniper tree?
Don't meddle! don't touch! little girl, little boy,
    Or the world will lose some of its joy.
        Now I'm glad! Now I'm free!
        And I always shall be,
If you never bring sorrow to me."

So the merry brown thrush sings away in the tree,
　To you and to me, to you and to me;
And he sings all the day, little girl, little boy,
　" Oh, the world's running over with joy;
　　But long it won't be,
　　Don't you know? Don't you see?
Unless we're as good as can be! "

Answer to a Child's Question

Samuel Taylor Coleridge

Do you know what the birds say? The sparrow, the
　dove,
The linnet and thrush say, " I love, and I love! "
In winter they're silent, the wind is so strong;
What it says I don't know, but it sings a loud song.
But green leaves, and blossoms, and sunny warm weather,
And singing and loving — all come back together.
But the lark is so brimful of gladness and love,
The green fields below him, the blue sky above,
That he sings, and he sings, and forever sings he,
" I love my love and my love loves me."

Lost — Three Little Robins

Anonymous

Oh, where is the boy dressed in jacket of gray,
Who climbed up a tree in the orchard to-day
And carried my three little birdies away?
　　They hardly were dressed,
　　When he took from the nest
My three little robins and left me distressed.

O wrens, have you seen in your travels to-day
A very small boy dressed in jacket of gray,
Who carried my three little robins away?
    He had light-colored hair,
    And his feet were both bare,
And he was most cruel to me, I declare.

O butterfly! stop just one moment, I pray;
Have you seen a small boy dressed in jacket of gray
Who carried my three little birdies away?
    From his pretty blue eyes
    One might think he was wise,
But he must be wicked for one of his size.

Bobolink! did you see my birdies and me,
How happy we were in the old apple tree,
Until I was robbed of my young, as you see?
    Oh, how can I sing,
    Unless he will bring
My three robins back, to sleep under my wing?

O boy with blue eyes dressed in jacket of gray!
If you will bring back my three robins to-day,
With sweetest of music the gift I'll repay;
    I'll sing all day long
    My merriest song,
And I will forgive you this terrible wrong.

Robin Redbreast

William Allingham

GOOD-BY, good-by to summer!
  For summer's nearly done;
The garden smiling faintly,
  Cool breezes in the sun;
Our thrushes now are silent,
  Our swallows flown away,—
But Robin's here, in coat of brown,
  And scarlet breast knot gay.
Robin, Robin Redbreast,
  O Robin dear!
Robin sings so sweetly
  In the falling of the year.

Bright yellow, red, and orange,
  The leaves come down in hosts;
The trees are Indian princes,
  But soon they'll turn to ghosts;
The scanty pears and apples
  Hang russet on the bough;
It's autumn, autumn, autumn late,
  'T will soon be winter now
Robin, Robin Redbreast,
  O Robin dear!
And what will this poor Robin do?
  For pinching days are near.

The fireside for the cricket,
  The wheat stack for the mouse,
When trembling night winds whistle
  And moan all round the house.

The frosty ways like iron,
  The branches plumed with snow,—
Alas! in winter dead and dark,
  Where can poor Robin go?
Robin, Robin Redbreast,
  O Robin dear!
Give a crumb of bread to Robin,
  His little heart to cheer.

September

Helen Hunt Jackson

THE goldenrod is yellow
  The corn is turning brown,
The trees in apple orchards
  With fruit are bending down.

The gentian's bluest fringes
  Are curling in the sun,
In dusky pods the milkweed
  Its hidden silk has spun.

The sledges flaunt their harvest
  In every meadow-nook,
And asters by the brookside
  Make asters in the brook.

From dewy lanes at morning
  The grapes' sweet odors rise.
At noon the roads all flutter
  With golden butterflies.

By all these lovely tokens
   September days are here,
With summer's best of weather
   And autumn's best of cheer.

Forest Song

W. H. Venable

A SONG for the beautiful trees,
A song for the forest grand,
The pride of His centuries,
The garden of God's own hand.
Hurrah for the kingly oak,
The maple, the forest queen,
The lords of the emerald cloak,
The ladies in living green.

For the beautiful trees a song,
The peers of a glorious realm,
So brave, and majestic, and strong,
The linden, the ash, and the elm.
Hurrah for the beech tree trim,
The hickory staunch at core,
The locust so thorny and grim,
And the silvery sycamore.

So long as the rivers flow,
So long as the mountains rise,
And shelter the earth below,
May the forest sing to the skies.
Hurrah! for the beautiful trees,
Hurrah! for the forest grand,
The pride of His centuries,
The garden of God's own hand.

Trees

Joyce Kilmer

I think that I shall never see
A poem lovely as a tree.

A tree whose hungry mouth is prest
Against the earth's sweet flowing breast;

A tree that looks at God all day
And lifts her leafy arms to pray;

A tree that may in summer wear
A nest of robins in her hair;

Upon whose bosom snow has lain;
Who intimately lives with rain.

Poems are made by fools like me,
But only God can make a tree.

From "*Trees and Other Poems*" by Joyce Kilmer.   Copyright, 1914, by George H. Doran Company, Publishers.

Thou shalt teach the ages, sturdy tree,
Youth of soul is immortality.
              —*Lucy Larcom.*

Tongues in trees, books in the running brooks,
Sermons in stones, and good in everything.
              —*Shakespeare.*

'Tis education forms the common mind;
Just as the twig is bent the tree's inclined.
              —*Pope.*

Quotations for Arbor and Bird Day

Summer or winter, day or night,
The woods are ever a new delight;
They give us peace, and they make us strong,
Such a wonderful balm to them belong:
So, living or dying, I'll take my ease
Under the trees, under the trees.

— R. H. Stoddard.

The groves were God's first temples.— *William Cullen Bryant.*

For every tree gives answer to some different mood;
This one helps you climb; that for rest is good;
Beckoning friends, companions, sentinels they are;
Good to live and die with, good to greet afar.

— Lucy Larcom.

The alder by the river
    Shakes out her powdery curls;
The willow buds in silver
    For little boys and girls.

— Celia Thaxter.

A glorious tree is the old gray oak;
He has stood for a thousand years,—
He has stood and frowned,
On the trees around,
Like a king among his peers.

— George Hill.

When April winds
Grew soft, the maple burst into a flush
Of scarlet flowers.

— William Cullen Bryant.

"The poplar drops beside the way
Its tasseled plumes of silver gray."

— Selected.

It is as if the pine-trees called me
From the ceiled room and silent brooks,
To see the dance of woodland shadows,
And hear the song of April brooks.
                    — *John G. Whittier.*

        By the swift river's flood
        The willow's golden blood
        Mounts to the higher spray,
        More vivid day by day.
                    — *Celia Thaxter.*

The pussy willows in their play,
Their varnished caps have flung away,
And hung their fur on every spray.
                    — *William W. Bailey.*

On all her boughs the stately chestnut cleaves
The gummy shroud that wraps her embryo leaves.
                    — *Oliver Wendell Holmes.*

Blow, winds! and waft through all the rooms
The snowflakes of the cherry-blooms!
                    — *Henry Wadsworth Longfellow.*

        A song for the beautiful trees!
        A song for the forest grand,
        The garden of God's own hand,
        The pride of His centuries.
                    — *W. H. Venable.*

The elm's vast shadow far and cool
    Fell o'er the dusty way,
Blessing the toilers at their rest,
    The children at their play.
                    — *M. F. Butts.*

But when the bare and wintry woods we see,
What then so cheerful as the Holly-tree?
                    — *Robert Southey.*

O hemlock tree! O hemlock tree, how faithful are thy
   branches!
Green not alone in summer time
But in the winter's frost and rime!
O hemlock tree! O hemlock tree, how faithful are thy
   branches.
   — Henry Wadsworth Longfellow.

Then shall the trees of the wood sing out at the presence
of the Lord.*— Bible.*

He who plants an oak looks forward to future ages, and
plants for posterity.*— Washington Irving.*

I hear from many a little throat,
   A warble interrupted long;
I hear the robin's flute-like note,
   The bluebird's slenderer song.
   — William Cullen Bryant.

Do you ne'er think what wondrous beings these?
Do you ne'er think who made them and who taught
The dialect they speak, where melodies
Alone are the interpreters of thought?
Whose household words are songs in many keys,
Sweeter than instruments of man e'er caught!
Whose habitations in the tree-tops even
Are half-way houses on the road to Heaven!
   — Henry Wadsworth Longfellow.

How pleasant the lives of the birds must be,
   Living in love in a leafy tree!
And away through the air what joy to go
   And look on the bright, green earth below!
   — Mary Howitt.

God sent his Singers upon earth
With songs of gladness and of mirth,
That they might touch the hearts of men,
And bring them back to heaven again.
　　　　　— Henry Wadsworth Longfellow.

The sweetest song the whole year 'round,—
'Tis the first robin in the Spring.
　　　　　— Clarence E. Stedman.

Up soared the lark into the air,
A shaft of song, a winged prayer,
As if a soul released from pain
Were flying back to Heaven again.
　　　　　— James Russell Lowell.

Sunshine set to music!
　Hear the sparrow sing!
In his note is freshness
　Of the new born Spring.
　　　　　— Lucy Larcom.

The swallow twitters about the eaves;
Blithely she sings, and sweet and clear.
　　　　　— Celia Thaxter.

O, Bluejay up in the maple tree,
Shaking your throat with such bursts of glee,
How did you happen to be so blue?
Did you steal a bit of the lake for your crest,
And fasten blue violets into your vest?
Tell me, I pray you,— tell me true!
　　　　　— Susan H. Sweet.

I know the song that the bluebird is singing —
Out in the appletree where he is swinging.
Brave little fellow! the skies may be dreary;
Nothing cares he while his heart is so cheery.
　　　　　— Emily H. Miller.

Don't kill the birds, the happy birds,
  That bless the fields and groves;
So innocent to look upon,
  They claim our warmest love.
                              — *Colesworthy.*

Merrily swinging on brier and weed,
  Near to the nest of his little dame,
Over the mountain side or mead,
  Robert of Lincoln is telling his name:
    " Bob-o'-link, bob-o'-link,
    Spink, spank, spink."
                    — *William Cullen Bryant.*

There is no rhyme that is half so sweet
As the song of the wind in the rippling wheat;
There is no meter that's half so fine
As the lilt of the brook under rock and vine;
And the loveliest lyric I ever heard
Was the wildwood strain of a forest bird.
                            — *Madison Cawein.*

" Oh, March, why are you scolding?
    Why not more cheerful be? "
" Because," said growling, blustering March,
    " The whole world scolds at me."
                                — *Selected.*

      In the urgent solitudes
      Lies the spur to larger moods;
      In the friendship of the trees
      Dwell all sweet serenities.
                        — *Ethelwyn Wetherald.*

Flower in the crannied wall,
I pluck you out of the crannies: —
Hold you here, root and all, in my hand,
Little flower, but if I could understand
What you are, root and all, and all in all,
I should know what God and man is.
                              — *Alfred Tennyson.*

A nation's growth from sea to sea
Stirs in his heart who plants a tree.
                    — Henry C. Bunner.

And there October passes
    In gorgeous livery —
In purple ash, and crimson oak,
    And golden tulip tree.
                    — Bliss Carman.

Up soared the lark into the air,
A shaft of song, a winged prayer,
As if a soul, released from pain,
Were flying back to heaven again.
                    — Henry Wadsworth Longfellow.

Teach me half the gladness
    That thy brain must know,
Such harmonious madness
    From my lips would flow,
The world should listen then,
    As I am listening now.
                    — Percy Bysshe Shelley.

Deep in the crimson afterglow,
We heard the homeward cattle low,
And then the far-off, far-off woe
Of " whippoorwill! " of " whippoorwill! "
                    — Madison J. Cawein.

He who, from zone to zone,
Guides through the boundless sky thy certain flight,
In the long way that I must tread alone,
Will lead my steps aright.
                    — William Cullen Bryant.

The happy birds, the tuneful birds,
How pleasant 'tis to see!
No spot can be a cheerless place
Where'er their presence be.
                    — Colesworthy.

ARMISTICE DAY

November 11

Armistice Day was first celebrated on November 11, 1918. Although it was somewhat dimmed by the fact that the signing of the Armistice had been erroneously announced and unrestrained festivities had taken place three days before, November 11, 1918, was fittingly celebrated by joyous demonstrations throughout the Allied armies and in every city, town and village of the Allied countries. November 11th was first designated as a national holiday in the United States in 1921 out of respect to the unknown American soldier, who was buried at Arlington (symbolic of the unidentified dead of the World War).

The Peace Call

Edgar Lloyd Hampton

I AM the voice of the uplands ringing from hill to hill,
Calling you back to action; hearken, and do my will.
Put up your spear and saber, smother the torch and
brand,
Lay down your weapons of warfare; come back, for
peace is at hand.
Back to your reeking workshop, turning again to toil;
Lift up the horn of plenty out of the teeming soil.
Shoulder the pick and shovel, kindle again the hearth,
Scatter the wheat and barley over the wasted earth.

For the cannon is hushed in the lowland, the order has
been withdrawn,
And the sound of disbanding armies echoes from dark
to dawn.
Up from the reeking byways come the sons and daugh-
ters of men,
Beating their swords and shrapnel back into plows
again.
Over the waste of the valley the sound of an anvil rings,
And up from the fields of carnage a blood-red poppy
springs.
And the shepherd is out on the hillside, calling again
to his sheep;
And the song of the busy sickle awakens the earth from
sleep.

Peace

Harold Trowbridge Pulsifer

THE cannon's voice is dumb,
The sword is sheathed again,
Homeward our legions come,—
Is it peace for the sons of men?

Peace for the troubled earth
And the host of those that lie
In the lands that gave them birth
Or beneath a stranger sky?

Shall children laugh for aye
And the sound of weeping cease
At the call of those who cry
Peace — when there is no peace?

Peace? What is peace but a name
For the war that shall not end
While souls are wrought in flame
High heaven to defend —?

Peace is a living sword
Forged for the hand of man
At the smithy of the Lord
In the halls where life began.

Peace is a challenge blown
In the trumpet of the wind.—
Till the stars are overthrown
Lift up your eyes, O blind!

And with your eyes mark well
God's banners swinging clear.
What do these banners tell?
To arms! For peace is here!

Peace

Henry Wadsworth Longfellow

WERE half the power that fills the world with terror,
  Were half the wealth bestowed on camps and courts,
Given to redeem the human mind from error,
  There were no need of arsenal or forts.
  The warrior's name would be a name abhorred;
  And every nation that should lift again
Its hand against a brother, on its forehead
  Would wear forevermore the curse of Cain!

The Christ of the Andes

Edwin Markham

AFTER volcanoes husht with snows,
Up where the wide-winged condor goes,
Great Aconcagua, husht and high,
Sends down the ancient peace of the sky.

So, poised in clean Andean air,
Where bleak with cliffs the grim peaks stare,
Christ, reaching out his sacred hands,
Sheds his brave peace upon the lands.

There once of old wild battles roared
And brother-blood was on the sword;

Now all the fields are rich with grain
And only roses redden the plain.

Torn were the peoples with feuds and hates —
Fear on the mountain-walls, death at the gates;
Then through the clamor of arms was heard
A whisper of the Master's word.

" Fling down your swords; be friends again:
Ye are not wolf-packs: ye are men.
Let brother-counsel be the Law:
Not serpent fang, not tiger claw."

Chile and Argentina heard;
The great hopes in their spirits stirred;
The red swords from their clenched fists fell,
And heaven shone out where once was hell!

They hurled their cannons into flame
And out of the forge the strong Christ came.
'Twas thus they molded in happy fire
The tall Christ of their heart's desire. . . .

O Christ of Olivet, you husht the wars
Under the far Andean stars:
Lift now your strong nail-wounded hands
Over all peoples, over all lands —
Stretch out those comrade hands to be
A shelter over land and sea!

From *New Poems* in preparation by Edwin Markham.

The Reign of Peace

Eliza Thornton

BEAUTIFUL vision! how bright it rose —
Vision of peaceful and calm repose!
Well might it brighten the rapt seer's eye,
And waken his heart to an ecstasy!
'Twas earth, glad earth, when her strife was o'er,
Her conflict ended, and war no more.

Households are grouped in the fig-tree's shade,
None to molest them or make afraid;
Securely rest 'neath the house-side vine
Parent and child from the noon sunshine;
Nations rejoice in the blest release,
And the voice of Earth is a voice of peace.

Beautiful vision; and shall it be
Surely accomplished, O Earth, in thee?
The sword of war, shall it scathe no more
The peaceful scenes of the softest shore?
And light stream down from the radiant skies
On scenes of the war god's sacrifice?

Ay! for the word of the prophet is true.
Fair was the vision; but full in view,
The Moslem's saber, all keen and bright,
Burnished and bare for the ready fight;
Sheath it he will, and in spirit be
Like the turtle dove in his cypress tree.

The vines of Judah shall then be pruned,
Her broken harp be again attuned;

And listening Earth, from her farthest shore,
Startled not now by the cannon's roar,
Songs of the angels shall hear again:
" Peace on earth, and good will to men!"

Peace Triumphant

Cale Young Rice

EARTH, Mother Earth, do you feel light flowing,
  Peace-light, waited so vainly and long?
Feel the great blood-eclipse guiltily going,
  Swept from your face by a tide too strong?
Over your rim is the bright flood rilling,
  Singing through air and under the seas.
Never since birth was such a beam-spilling,
  Never such warmth, such healing and ease.
Wildly it wraps you, and, oh, your children
  Open their heart-gates to the glad rays.
Blood-gloom there was, blindness, and hating;
  Now there is wonder, relief, and amaze.

Earth, Mother Earth, it will loose away from you
  Pestilence, famine, horror, and pain.
Cleanse, and of loathed inhumanity calm you,
  Giving your veins well-being again.
Sleep shall come back to your cities, chalets,
  To ships in the night when the watch-bell sounds —
Sleep, the one opiate soothing nature,
  Sleeplessly pours upon mortal wounds.
Sleep in the night and peace in the morning!
  Under their cool, strong febrifuge,
Soon shall you swing again to clear ether,
  Hopeful, though the price paid be huge.

Yes, Mother Earth, you have suffered, but sorrow
    Has brought you at last what *it* alone can.
Races you had that raged; but to-morrow
    Men on your sphere shall behold but man.
Nations you had, all strifefully claiming
    Food at your breast and place in your arms,
Isles that bejeweled you, and broad empire
    Over your lesser children swarms;
Nations you had, but now to one nation
    Fast they are merging, ready to say
For the first time there is but one mother
Of men, to be cherished by them alway!

From the *Century Magazine*.

Peace Universal

Anna H. Thorne

Gift of the living God to mortal man;
A bridge, the gates of life and death to span.

A stir, a breath, a dream, a fantasy,
The silent, onward tread of destiny.

Thy Promised One, oh, man! majestic, sweet;
The fires of dawn still clinging to her feet.

Thine, man, to have and hold, if thou dost choose;
Everything to gain, and all to lose.

Sphinx-like, yet beautiful, about her face
Linger the star-flowers of a nameless grace.

Oh, joy bells! ring the noble message forth;
Flash it, electric currents, to the North,

The South, the subtle East, the stalwart West;
From sea to sea, from mountain crest to crest.

"*Peace Universal*," shall thy watchword be —
The touchstone of thy Christianity.

Sheathe thou the sword, the dying century's shame;
Quench, in man's love to man, the lurid battle flame.

Where is the interpreter who shall arise
To write my message on the changeless skies?

I am the genius of the age to be;
My name is Peace; my guerdon, Opportunity.

These are my words, oh, man! All nations of the earth
Are of one blood, one consecrated birth.

Where is the conqueror at whose knightly tread
The tiger hounds of war shall crouch in dread?

At sight of whom, like some archangel mild,
Or some new vision of the Holy Child,

Old wrongs shall perish and pass out of sight
Into the darkness of an endless night?

Peace

G. O. Warren

PEACE, battle-worn and starved, and gaunt and pale
Rises like mist upon a storm-swept shore.
Rises from out the blood-stained fields and bows her
    head,
Blessing the passionate dead
Who gladly died that she might live for evermore.

Unheeding generations come and go,
And careless men and women will forget,
Caught in the whirling loom who tapestried To-day
Flings Yesterday away,
And covers up the crimsoned West whose sun has set.

But faithful ghosts, like shepherds, will return
To call the flocking shades and break with them
Love-bread, and Peace will strain them to her breast, and
    weep,
And deathless vigil keep.
Yea, Peace, while worlds endure, will sing their requiem.

When the Cannon Booms No More

William Herbert Carruth

WHEN the cannon booms,
  When the war-drums rattle fiercely
And the feet of men in khaki hammer time out on the
    pave,
  It is easy to be brave;
It is easy to believe that God is angry with the other Man,
    our brother,

And has left the sword of Gideon in our wayward
human hand,
When the cannon booms.

When the cannon booms,
When the primal love of fighting stirs the tiger in our
blood,
And the fascinating smell
Of the sulphur-fumes of hell
Rouses memories of the pit from which our human
nature rose,
It is easy to forget
God was not found in the earthquake, in the strong wind
or the fire,
It is easy to forget how at last the prophet heard Him
As a still, small voice,
When the cannon booms.

When the cannon booms,
When the war lords strut and swagger
And the battle-ships are plowing for the bitter crop of
death,
While the shouting rends the ear,
Echoing from the empyrean,
It is difficult to hear
Through the din the Galilean
With his calm voice preaching peace on earth to men;
'Twill be easier to claim,
If we will, the Christian name,
To become as little children and be men of gentle will,
When the cannon booms — the cannon booms no more.

From *Each in His Own Tongue*. By permission of G. P.
Putnam's Sons, Publishers, New York and London.

The New City

Marguerite O. B. Wilkinson

HAVE we seen her, the New City, O my brothers, where
    she stands,
The superb, supreme creation of unnumbered human
    hands:
The complete and sweet expression of unnumbered hu-
    man souls,
Bound by love to work together while their love their
    work controls;
Built by brothers for their brothers, kept by sisters for
    their mates,
Garlanded by happy children playing free within the
    gates,
Brooded by such mighty mothers as are born to lift
    us up
Till we drink in full communion of God's wondrous
    " loving cup ";
Clean and sightly are her pavements ringing sound be-
    neath men's feet,
Wide and ample are her forums where her citizens may
    meet,
Fair and precious are her gardens where her youths and
    maidens dance
In the fresh, pure air of Heaven, 'mid the flowers' ex-
    travagance.
And her schools are as the ladders to the Spirit, from
    the Clay,
Leading, round by round, to labor, strengthened side
    by side, by play,
And her teachers are her bravest, and her governors
    her best,

For she loves the little children she has nourished at
her breast.

Never clangor of the trumpet, nor the hiss of bullets
mad

Breaks the music of her fountain, plashing seaward,
flashing glad,

For no excess and no squalor mark her fruitful, fair
increase —

She has wrought life's final glory in a miracle of peace;

And her citizens live justly, without gluttony or need,

And he strives to serve the city who has bread enough
to feed

All his own, and she must labor, who would hold an
honored place

With the women of the city in their dignity and grace,

Have ye seen her, O my brothers, the New City, where
each hour

Is a poet's revelation, or a hero's perfect power,

Or an artist's new creation, or a laborer's new strength,

Where a world of aspiration clings God by the feet, at
length?

Have ye seen her, the New City, in her glory? Ah,
not yet

Gilds the sun with actual splendor chimney top and
minaret,

But her sight is surely purchased and her pattern is designed,

And her blessed ways are visions for all striving human-
kind!

The New City, O my brothers, we ourselves shall never
see —

She will gladden children's children into holy ecstasy —

Let our lives be in the building! We shall lay us in
the sod,

Happier, if our human travail builds their avenues to
God!

From the *Independent*.

Quotations for Armistice Day

Down the dark future, through long generations,
  The echoing sounds grow fainter, and then cease;
And like a bell, with solemn, sweet vibrations,
  I hear once more the voice of Christ say, "Peace!"

Peace! and no longer from its brazen portals
  The blast of War's great organ shakes the skies!
But, beautiful as songs of the immortals,
  The holy melodies of love arise.
                — *Henry Wadsworth Longfellow.*

The cost of war and of armed peace is still larger in the
civilized countries of the world than the cost of schools and
of other formal means of education. Were it possible to
deliver the world immediately from this burden of an outgrown and antiquated institution by bringing in the reign of
reason, good will, and constructive cooperation, the opportunities for education might at once be increased from two
to four fold throughout the world without any increase in
the total burden of taxation.— *P. P. Claxton.*

New arts shall bloom, of loftier mould,
  And mightier music thrill the skies;
And every life shall be a song,
  When all the earth is paradise.

There shall be no more sin nor shame,
  And wrath and wrong shall fettered lie;
For man shall be at one with God
  In bonds of firm necessity.
                — *J. Addington Symonds.*

My first wish is to see the whole world at peace and the inhabitants of it as one band of brothers, striving which should contribute most to the happiness of mankind.— *George Washington.*

The ever-growing armaments of civilized nations are leading toward national bankruptcy. Colossal expenditures on armies and navies can never secure happiness and prosperity. Armaments beget hatred, fear, and insecurity of trade. On the other hand, all nations benefit by commerce and friendly intercourse. Interruption of these means ruin to the workers and desolation in many homes. The true patriot seeks the extension of international friendship, remembering that the nations are looking to America to lead them in this great movement.— *Selected.*

The development of the doctrine of international arbitration, considered from the standpoint of its ultimate benefits to the human race, is the most vital movement of modern times. In its relation to the well-being of the men and women of this and ensuing generations, it exceeds in importance the proper solution of various economic problems which are constant themes of legislative discussion or enactment.— *William Howard Taft.*

> Oh! make thou us through centuries long,
> In Peace secure, in Justice strong:
> Around our gift of Freedom, draw
> The safeguards of thy righteous law;
> And cast in some diviner mould,
> Let the new cycle shame the old.
> — *John G. Whittier.*

For ye shall go out with joy, and be led forth with peace: the mountains and the hills shall break forth before you into singing, and all the trees of the field shall clap their hands. Instead of the thorn shall come up the fir tree, and instead of the brier shall come up the myrtle tree; and it shall be to the Lord for a name, for an everlasting sign that shall not be cut off.— *Isaiah 55 : 12, 13.*

And God shall judge between the nations,
And arbitrate for many people;
He shall make their officers peace, and their rulers right-
    eousness;
And they shall beat their swords into ploughshares,
And their spears into pruning-hooks;
Nation shall not lift up sword against nation,
Neither shall they have war any more.

— *Scriptures.*

RED CROSS DAY

Red Cross Day is not a legal holiday but there is a certain time set aside each year to collect funds by popular subscription in order that the American Red Cross Society may continue its good work of bringing relief to millions throughout the world. The schools have helped this cause to a considerable extent through their support of the Junior Red Cross Society.

The Soldier of the Silences

William Herschell

SWEET Soldier of the Silences! You who, in garb of
white,
You who, from Lens and Verdun, bring our bullet-bat-
tered men
To feel the magic of your touch and make them whole
again;
In you we lay a master-faith and pledge that faith anew
As each day makes more glorious the martyrdom of you

Sweet Soldier of the Silences! You've left your all be-
hind
To make the sad become the glad; to comfort, soothe, and
bind.
While others calmly slumber you must ever be alert
To catch the slightest murmur that reveals a restless hurt.
How calm you are in trying hours, how glad you are
to share
Another's pain and with your smile make pain less hard
to bear.

Sweet Soldier of the Silences! Adown the long white
aisle
You tiptoe all unmindfully of the hour or day or mile;
A bandage here, a tuck-in there, a drink, a touch of hand
That only soldiers such as ours have soul to understand.
Your Red Cross emblem they'll defend through stress of
of time and tide;
It is God's goodness manifest — Old Glory sanctified!

The League of Love in Action

Edwin Markham

O LEAGUE of Kindness, woven in all lands,
You bring Love's tender mercies in your hands;
Above all flags you lift the conquering sign,
And hold invincible Love's battle line.

O League of Kindness, in your far-flung bands,
You weave a chain that reaches to God's hands;
And where blind guns are plotting for the grave,
Yours are the lips that cheer, the arms that save.

O League of Kindness, in your flag we see
A foregleam of the brotherhood to be
In ages when the agonies are done,
When all will love and all will lift as one.

(Author of " The Man with the Hoe and Other Poems.")

The Great Cross of Mercy

Theodosia Garrison

GLORIOUS with scars and rents the battle-banners rise,
And the great flags of triumph are spreading to the skies
Our tears, our prayers, our praise for them, but when
    the last is said
Our hearts extol the banner that bears the Cross of Red.

The great Cross of Mercy that calls a world in pain
To lift its soul to courage, to look on hope again —
The sign of Love victorious that hate hath never slain.

Ask those who have waited it upon the fields of strife,
Ask the stricken towns-folk it has given back to life,
Ask the lips of childhood, the valiant hosts of dead
What this banner means to them that bears the Cross of
　　Red.

The Great Cross of Mercy — O lift and keep it high,
Send its flaming message to all humanity
That Pity is immortal and that Love shall never die.

The Red Cross

Henry Van Dyke

Sign of the Love Divine
　　That bends to bear the load
Of all who suffer, all who bleed,
　　Along life's thorny road.

Sign of the Heart Humane,
　　That through the darkest fight
Would bring to wounded friend and foe
　　A ministry of light.

O dear and holy sign,
　　Lead onward like a star,
The armies of the just are thine,
　　And all we have and are.

The Army of the Red Cross

Katrina Trask

THROUGH carnage, desolation, blood and mire,
'Mid scenes that cry to an avenging God,
The Red Cross Army moves through scathing fire —
Clothed in white garments, with quick mercy shod.
Commissioned is that Army from above:
Its standard is a Cross, its watchword — Love.

Dead are the crosses condescending kings
Bestow on martial men who bravely fight:
They are but decorations — lifeless things.
The Red Cross is a living cross of Light:
It shines where men in mortal anguish lie,
It glows, a gleaming guidon, from on high.

The Red Cross Nurses

Thomas L. Masson

OUT where the line of battle cleaves
The horizon of woe,
And sightless warriors clutch the leaves,
The Red Cross nurses go.
In where the cots of agony
Mark death's unmeasured tide —
Bear up the battle's harvestry —
The Red Cross nurses glide.

Look! Where the hell of steel has torn
Its way through slumbering earth,
The orphaned urchins kneel forlorn

And wonder at their birth.
Until, above them, calm and wise,
With smile and guiding hand,
God looking through their gentle eyes,
The Red Cross nurses stand.

The Red Cross Nurse

Edith M. Thomas

THE battle-smoke still fouled the day,
    With bright disaster flaming through;
Unchecked, absorbed, she held her way —
    The whispering death still past her flew.

A cross of red was on her sleeve;
    And here she stayed, the wound to bind,
And there, the fighting soul relieve,
    That strove its Unknown Peace to find.

A cross of red . . . yet one has dreamed
    Of her he loved and left in tears;
But unto dying sight she seemed
    A visitant from other spheres.

The whispering death — it nearer drew,
    It holds her heart in strict arrest . . .
And where was one, are crosses two —
    A crimson cross is on her breast!

If Ever Time Shall Come

Alison Brown

IF ever time shall come when I can see
A crimson cross against a field of white,
And fail to hear the words it speaks to me,
Lord, pierce my spirit with the sword of Light.

And let me glimpse the vision once again,
For Jesus' sake a cup of water given;
And in His name relief from weary pain,
And mercy, tender snowy-winged from Heaven.

And where it hovers o'er the battle line,
The symbol of a mighty mother's care,
May I not say the crimson cross is mine,
If I have helped to place its banner there?

Santa Filomena

Henry W. Longfellow

WHENE'ER a noble deed is wrought,
Whene'er is spoken a noble thought,
  Our hearts, in glad surprise,
  To higher levels rise.

The tidal wave of deeper souls
Into our inmost being rolls,
  And lifts us unawares
  Out of all meaner cares.

Honor to those whose words or deeds
Thus help us in our daily needs,
    And by their oveflow
    Raise us from what is low!

Thus thought I, as by night I read
Of the great army of the dead,
    The trenches cold and damp,
    The starved and frozen camp,—

The wounded from the battle-plain
In dreary hospitals of pain,
    The cheerless corridors,
    The cold and stony floors.

Lo! in that house of misery
A lady with a lamp [1] I see
    Pass through the glimmering gloom,
    And flit from room to room.

And slow, as in a dream of bliss,
The speechless sufferer turns to kiss
    Her shadow, as it falls
    Upon the darkening walls.

As if a door in heaven should be
Opened and then closed suddenly,
    The vision came and went,
    The light shone and was spent.

On England's annals, through the long
Hereafter of her speech and song,
    That light its rays shall cast
    From portals of the past.

[1] Florence Nightingale, founder of modern nursing.

A Lady with a Lamp shall stand
In the great history of the land,
  A noble type of good,
  Heroic womanhood.

Nor even shall be wanting here
The palm, the lily, and the spear,
  The symbols that of yore
  Saint Filomena bore.

By permission of, and by special arrangement with, Houghton Mifflin Co.

The Three Crosses

Edmund Vance Cook

THE iron cross is black as death and hard as human hate;
The wooden cross is white and still and whispers us " Too late ";
But the Red Cross sings of life and love and hearts regenerate.

The iron cross is a boastful cross and marks a war-mad slave;
The wooden cross is a dumb, dead cross and guards a shallow grave,
But the Red Cross reaches out its arms to solace and to save.

The iron cross is a kaiser's cross and narrow is its clan,
The wooden cross is a soldier's cross and mourns its partisan,
But the Red Cross is the Cross of One who served his fellowmen.

Your Cross and My Cross

Emma Finty Cox

YOUR boy and my boy,
And how they go to-day
From your home and my home
To the trenches far away!
Brave lads and true lads,
They never think of fear;
Young men and strong men —
We hold them all so dear;
And the one cross, the Red Cross. the cross for me and
    you,
Will succor them in every land 'neath the red and white
    and blue.

Your heart and my heart
Throb as though to break,
While your hands and my hands
Garments of comfort make.
Your thoughts and my thoughts
Follow them each day;
To your God and my God
For them we fondly pray;
And the one cross, the Red Cross, the cross for me and
    you,
Will succor them in every land 'neath the red and white
    and blue.

Your food and my food
We now must guard and save,
That " Your Flag and my Flag "
May ever proudly wave.

Your Gold and my Gold,
Of it we freely give,
That your son and my son
In foreign climes may live;
And the one cross, the Red Cross, the cross for me and
    you,
Will succor them in every land 'neath the red and white
    and blue.

Somebody's Boy

Katherine Lee Bates

SOMEBODY'S boy, his young face gray,
Lies where the shells, in demon play,
Fling up fountains of ruddy spray,
    Splinter and tear and toss.
Bleeding he waits on Death's wild whim,
But stretcher-bearers have lifted him
Back through the shrapnel, over the rim
    Of the trench.   O brave Red Cross!

Somebody's boy, his wildered brain
Waking from ether, stabbed with pain,
Smiles to a touch as cool as rain
    Falling on sun-parched moss,
Smiles to the white-garbed nurse who bends
Over his broken body, mends
Horror with kindness, best of friends
    To our soldiers, dear Red Cross!

Somebody's boy, beyond the war,
In that happier world he has battled for,
Love the Lord and the conqueror,

Shall turn from the tarnished gloss
Of idle cannon and bayonet
To greet, on its errands of mercy yet,
His hand at salute and lashed wet,
    Christ's chivalry, Red Cross!

The Red Cross Spirit Speaks

John E. Finley

I

WHENEVER war, with its red woes,
Or flood, or fire or famine goes,
    There, too, go I;
If earth in any quarter quakes,
Or pestilence its ravage makes,
    Thither I fly.

II

I kneel behind the soldier's trench,
I walk 'mid shambles' smear and stench,
    The dead I mourn;
I bear the stretcher and I bend
O'er Fritz and Pierre and Jack to mend
    What shells have torn.

III

I go wherever men may dare,
I go wherever woman's care
    And love can live,
Wherever strength and skill can bring
Surcease to human suffering
    Or solace give.

IV

I helped upon Haldora's shore,
With Hospitaller Knights I bore
 The first red cross;
I was the Lady of the Lamp
I saw in Solferino's camp
 The crimson loss.

V

I am your pennies and your pounds,
I am your bodies on their rounds
 Of pain afar;
I am *you* doing what you would
If you were only where you could —
 Your avatar.

VI

The cross which on my arm I wear,
The flag which o'er my breast I bear,
 Is but the sign
Of what you'd sacrifice for him
Who suffers on the hellish rim
 Of war's red line.

NOTE: Extract from Mabel T. Boardman's book "Under the Red Cross Flag":

"A touch of the Red Cross spirit manifested itself after a battle a thousand years ago, when Haldora of Iceland called to the women of her household, 'Let us go and dress the wounds of the warriors, be they friends or foes.'"

The Medical Corps

Beatrice Barry

THEIR country's need is more to them than personal de-
    mands:
There is no law to send these men to serve in war-torn
    lands;
They freely go, they gladly go, with healing in their
    hands.

What is the sacrifice they make? A life's achievements
    lost;
The barriers that blocked success by weary stages crossed,
They cast the hard-won prize aside, nor stop to count the
    cost.
I think the surgeons, more than most, are truly great of
    soul;
Their many charities, if told, would fill a lengthy scroll —
Their daily, countless kindnesses make more than bodies
    whole.

God speed the ships that bear the food we hasten over-
    seas;
God bless the men who fight to save our threatened lib-
    erties —
God knows the surgeons who enlist are not the least of
    these.

Compensation

Ruth Comfort Mitchell

ALL those dark days in spring when we would sew
  At the Red Cross, all this racked, crawling year,
  She was serene, unclouded: no one near
Or necessary to her had to go.
She could roll bandages and never know
  The black imaginings . . . the choking fear. . . .
  I envied her her placid face, her cheer,
With a hot envy molten in my woe.

But now, with a red world washed white in peace,
  Where life and love flow warmly back to me,
She knows no leaping rapture, no release,
  No sanctuary in a holy place,
And I speak softly that she may not see
  My surging pity for her placid face!

From *Harper's Magazine.*

The Red Cross Christmas Seal

Theodosia Garrison

OH, happy folk, contented folk, and ye that go with gold
  To seek within the noisy mart the gifts to mark the day—
Jolly toys and gems and lace and trinkets manifold —
  Here be better wares to buy along the crowded way.

Buy a pair of red cheeks to give a little lad again,
  Buy a pallid woman's face the bright eyes of health,
Buy a broken man a hope, buy the strength he had again,
  Here are bargains wonderful awaiting on your wealth.

Oh, happy folk and careless folk, the world's bazaar is
    piled
With lovely gifts and lasting gifts to mark a holiday.
You who seek the fairest thing for lover, friend and child,
    Surely ye shall pause awhile and buy the while ye stay.

Buy a mother back her bairn, buy a man his wife again,
    Buy a lad the right to love, a child the right to play,
Buy the wistful kindred all, home and health and life
    again,
    And God be with you gentle-folk who purchase these
    today.

Quotations for Red Cross Day

My mission is of mercy, kindness, and charity. I am my
brother's keeper. I know neither color, race, nor religion.
My creed is the creed of service. My goal is the goal of a
higher humanity."

                                    — *Captain James A. Mills.*

Down across the ages comes the one voice of healing that
has ever blessed mankind, and in infinite pathos and beauty
it falls upon the lives of men, and it says:
  " Inasmuch as ye have done it unto the least of these, my
Brethren, ye have done it unto me."

                                    — *L. C. Hodgson.*

The Red Cross stands on a white ground, because real
sacrifice can come only from pure hearts. Service must
come, not from hate, but from love; from the noblest
thoughts and wishes of the heart.

                                    — *Dr. H. N. MacCracken.*

The vast international work of mercy which the Red
Cross conducts is an overwhelming evidence that idealism **in**

the heart of the race has not perished, for sympathy and love have never before taken such practical forms.

— Hamilton W. Mabie.

" Consecrated to the needs of humanity and inspired by the love of man for his fellow, I go forth to help the unfortunate, to make strong the weak, to teach the gospel of clean living and well being."

— Red Cross Bulletin.

The Red Cross is civilization's most effective agency for relief to-day.— *H. E. French.*

The Red Cross is fast becoming a vital force throughout the world — a force that is bringing the nations closer together in the bonds of human sympathy, brotherhood, and peace. Its work deserves to be known as the handmaiden of arbitration.—*George Griswold Hill.*

The Red Cross is a living cross of Light.— *Katrina Trask.*

This wonderful Red Cross is no temporary charity,— it is the spirit of Humanity spreading its blessing upon the souls of mankind.— *L. C. Hodson.*

It is the tie that binds the far separated acts of service together, until the little trickles of humanity shall all come together in a vast stream of human sympathy so pure and powerful as to accomplish a new thing on earth.— *Red Cross Magazine.*

O, you who have a mother dear,
  Let not a word or act give pain;
But cherish, love her, with your life,—
  You ne'er can have her like again.

— *Selected.*

MOTHERS' DAY

May —

The second Sunday in May has been designated as Mother's Day in honor of our mothers, living or dead. At this time of year appropriate sermons are delivered in the churches throughout the country, and the school children everywhere are taught a greater love and reverence for their mothers.

My Mother

Samuel N. Wilson

HER arms first cradled me with mother love and care;
Her eyes first beamed their welcome to my sight;
Her voice was sweetest lullaby by day and night;
Her faith taught me to lisp the name of God in prayer;
Her ear, alert to catch my cry of grief or pain;
Her hand, outstretched with cheer, my feeble steps to
   guide;
Her heart, so quick to note my growth, with joy and
   pride;
Her hope, full high, that I should wear the wreath of
   fame;

And yet, my mother, it was not the pomp of earth,
You longed to know that in life's battle I had won.
You rather wished for me the Master's word, "Well
   done";
You on His altar placed my life from hour of birth;
You caught the glint of holy things, the things unseen;
You taught my feet to tread the paths that upward go;
You gave me strength to breast the tides that ebb and
   flow;
You held before my eyes the Christ life, goal supreme.

"All that I have and all I hope to be" in life,
I gladly lay in loving tribute at your feet,
And on this Mothers' Day my heart doth hail and greet

You, queen! and pledge its fealty 'mid peace or strife.
Your feet are growing weary, for the path is long,
nd silver threads gleam white where the dark tresses
  lay;
few more years to cherish here — then break of day
heaven's glory greets you with its welcome song.

The White Carnation

Margaret E. Sangster

HERE's to the white carnation,
  Sturdy and spicy and sweet,
Wafting a breath of perfume
  On the stony way of the street;
Bringing a thought of gladness
  Wherever the breezes blow;
Here's to the white carnation,
  Pure as the virgin snow.

This is the flower for Mother,
  Wear it on Mothers' Day;
Flower for rain and sunshine,
  Winsome, gallant and gay;
Wear it in mother's honor
  Pinned to the coat's lapel;
Wear it in belt and corsage,
  For her who loved you well.

The mother in lowly cabin,
  The mother in palace hall,
Is ever the best and dearest,
  The one we love best of all,

In travail and pain she bore us,
　In laughter and love she nursed,
And who that would shame a mother
　Is of all mankind accursed.

Tired and wan too often,
　Weary and weak at times,
But always full of the courage
　That thrills when the future chimes;
Mother with hands toil-hardened,
　Mother in pearls and lace,
The light of heavenly beauty
　Shines in your tender face.

So here's to the white carnation,
　Wear it on Mothers' Day;
Flower that blooms for mother,
　Winsome, gallant and gay.
Flower of perfect sweetness,
　Flower for hut and hall,
Here's to the white carnation
　And to Mother — Our Best of All.

Little Mother

M. P. D.

To live without you, seems to me
Impossible, I cannot see
My way ahead, I only know
From day to day I stumbling go.

Yet this I feel, that thou art near,
And thy great love, which was so dear,

Will pierce the shadow, as the star
Shines out from darkest night afar.

So you will be, my dearest one,
My guiding star as years go on,
And some day, in that heaven above,
My heart again will find your love.

Her Little Boy

Pearson's Weekly

ALWAYS a " little boy " to her,
  No matter how old he's grown,
Her eyes are blind to the strands of gray,
  She's deaf to his manly tone.
His voice is the same as the day he asked,
  " What makes the old cat purr? "
Ever and ever he's just the same —
  A little boy to her.

Always a " little boy " to her,
  She heeds not the lines of care
That furrow his face — to her it is still
  As it was in his boyhood, fair;
His hopes and his joys are as dear to her
  As they were in his small-boy days,
He never changes; to her he's still
  " My little boy," she says.

Always a " little boy " to her,
  And to him she's the mother fair,
With the laughing eyes and the cheering smile
  Of the boyhood days back there.

Back there, somewhere in the midst of years —
　　Back there with the childish joy,
And to her he is never the man we see,
　　But always " her little boy."

Always a " little boy " to her,
　　The ceaseless march of the years
Goes rapidly by, but its drumbeats die
　　Ere ever they reach her ears.
The smile that she sees is the smile of youth,
　　The wrinkles are dimples of joy,
His hair with its gray is as sunny as May,
　　He is always " her little boy."

You Mean My Mother

Anonymous

IF I were asked to give a thought which in one word
　　would speak
A unity of brotherhood, a sympathy complete,
A hundred happy cheery ways, a mind that knows its own,
Contented midst a throng of folk, yet peaceful when
　　alone,
A heart that sheds its silent glow, to brighten many an-
　　other,
Without a moment of delay, I'd say, " You mean my
　　mother."

Our Mother

Anonymous

How oft some passing word will tend
    In visions to recall
Our truest, dearest, fondest friend —
    That earliest friend of all.

Who tended on our childish years,
    Those years that pass as hours,
When all earth's dewy, trembling tears,
    Lie hid within her flowers.

Thou star that shines in darkest night,
    When most we need thy aid,
Nor changes but to beam more bright
    When others coldly fade.

O Mother! round thy hallowed name
    Such blissful memory springs,
The heart in all but years the same,
    With reverent worship clings.

Thy voice was first to greet us, when
    Bright fortune smiling o'er us,
And thine the hand that's readiest then
    To lift the veil before us.

Or if dark clouds close round our head
    And care steals o'er the brow,
While hope's fair flowers fall crushed and dead
    Unchangéd still art thou.

Mother

Percy Waxman

Each day you live
Means one day more of life to her.
Each thought you give
Means more than honors can confer.
Each letter sent
Brings her a joy that floods her heart
With sweet content,
And makes her proud to do her part;
But, oh! the skies
Are black if death should claim you, son,
For mother dies
Ten thousand deaths when you die one.

A Mother Thought

Edgar A. Guest

Oh, my laddie! Oh, my laddie!
  Can't you hear me bravely singing
As I tuck the covers 'round you,
  Or a drink to you I'm bringing?
Do you hear me in the night-time
  When you call in dreams that fright,
Saying: " Go to sleep, my laddie,
  It will very soon be light "?

Oh, my laddie! Oh, my laddie!
  Don't you know that I am near you?
Have the hands that once caressed you
  Lost the mother gift to cheer you?

Do you think the dreary distance
  Keeps the heart of me away?
Can't you hear me calling to you
  As I called but yesterday?

Oh, my laddie! Oh, my laddie!
  I have followed where you wander.
Here the flesh of me is dwelling,
  But my soul is with you yonder.
Yes, my soul to you is singing
  All the lullabies you knew,
In the days before this danger
  Made a soldier boy of you.

Oh, my laddie! Oh, my laddie!
  Through the trials now before you,
Through the perils of the night-time
  I shall still be watching o'er you.
Can't you feel my mother fingers
  Smooth the hair about your brow?
Can't you see me, oh, my laddie,
  Standing there beside you now?

The Mother

Sarah Louise Arnold

SOME there be that sow the seed and reap the golden
    grain;
  And some there be that buy and sell, and find therein
    their gain;
And some do build with skilful craft; and some with
    curious art

Do paint or carve; and some do sing. So each doth
do his part.

And some there be — most blessed these — to deeds of
mercy given;
And some do heal the sick, and some do lead the way to
Heaven;
But holiest task of all is thine, oh Mother with thy
child!
For thee and him all workers toil, all craftsmen carve
and build.

Make pure thy heart, oh Mother-saint, that pure thy
son's may be;
Make strong thy soul, with courage strong, that he may
learn of thee;
Make true thy word, thy thought, thy deed, that truth may
make him free;
And pour thy noble life for his!   Thus safe our land
shall be.

Nobody Knows — But Mother

The Fireside

NOBODY knows of the work it makes
To keep the home together,
Nobody knows of the steps it takes,
Nobody knows — but mother.

Nobody listens to childish woes,
Which kisses only smother;
Nobody's pained by naughty blows,
Nobody — only mother.

Nobody knows of the sleepless care
  Bestowed on baby brother;
Nobody knows of the tender prayer,
  Nobody — only mother.

Nobody knows of the lessons taught
  Of loving one another;
Nobody knows of the patience sought,
  Nobody — only mother.

Nobody knows of the anxious fears,
  Lest darlings may not weather
The storm of life in after years,
  Nobody knows — but mother.

Nobody kneels at the throne above
  To thank the Heavenly Father
For that sweetest gift — a mother's love;
  Nobody can — but mother.

The Echo of a Song

J. W. Foley

To my fancy, idly roaming, comes a picture of the gloam-
    ing,
  Comes a fragrance from the blossoms of the lilac and
    the rose;
With the yellow lamplight streaming I am sitting here and
    dreaming
Of a half-forgotten twilight whence a mellow memory
    flows;
To my listening ears come winging vagrant notes of
    woman's singing;

I've a sense of sweet contentment as the sounds are
    borne along;
'Tis a mother who is tuning her fond heart to love and
    crooning
  To her laddie such a
                    Sleepy little
                        Creepy little
                            Song.

Ah, how well do I remember when by crackling spark and
    ember
  The old-fashioned oaken rocker moved with rhythmic
    sweep and slow;
With her feet upon the fender, in a cadence low and
    tender,
  Floated forth that slumber anthem of a childhood long
    ago.
There were goblins in the gloaming, and the half-closed
    eyes went roaming
  Through the twilight for the ghostly shapes of bugaboos
    along;
Now the sandman's slyly creeping and a tired lad's half
    sleeping,
  When she sings to him that
                    Sleepy little
                        Creepy little
                            Song.

So I'm sitting here and dreaming with the mellow lamp-
    light streaming
  Through the vine-embowered window in a yellow fili-
    gree,
On the fragrant air come winging vagrant notes of wom-
    an's singing,

'Tis the slumber song of childhood that is murmuring
    to me,
And some subtle fancy creeping lulls my senses half to
    sleeping
As the misty shapes of bugaboos go dreamily along,
All my sorrows disappearing, as a tired lad I'm hearing
    Once again my mother's
                Sleepy little
                      Creepy little
                          Song.

From " Boy and Girls," published by E. P. Dutton & Co.

Ma's Tools

Anonymous

At home it seems to be the rule
Pa never has " the proper tool "
Or knack to fix things.   For the stunt
That stumps ma, though, you'll have to hunt.

The caster on the table leg
Fell out.   Pa said a wooden peg
Would fix it up.   But ma kep' mum
An' fixed it with a wad of gum.

We could scarce open our front door,
It stuck so tight.   An' pa, he swore
He'd " buy a plane " as big as life —
Ma fixed it with the carving-knife.

The bureau drawer got stuck one day,
An', push or pull, 'twas there to stay.

Says pa, " Some day 'twill shrink, I hope."
Ma fixed it with a piece of soap.

The window-shade got out of whack,
'Twould not pull down, nor yet roll back,
Pa says, " No one can fix *that* thing."
Ma fixed it with a piece of string.

I broke the stove-door hinge one day.
('Twas cracked before, though, anyway.)
Pa said we'd put a new door in.
Ma grabbed her hair an' got a pin.

The bath-tub drain got all clogged up.
Pa bailed the tub out with a cup —
He had a dreadful helpless look.
Ma cleaned it with a crochet-hook.

One day our old clock wouldn't start,
Pa said he'd take it all apart
Some day an' fix the ol' machine.
Ma soused the works in gasoline.

The garden gate latch broke one day,
Cows ate our sweet corn up. An', say,
Pa scolded like a house afire!
Ma fixed the latch up with hay wire.

So when my things gets out of fix
Do I ask pa to mend 'em? Nix!
But ma just grabs what's near at hand
An' togs things up to beat the band.

My Mother

Anonymous

Who fed me from her gentle breast
And hushed me in her arms to rest,
And on my cheek sweet kisses prest?
    My mother.

When sleep forsook my open eye,
Who was it sung sweet lullaby
And rocked me that I should not cry?
    My mother.

Who sat and watched my infant head
When sleeping in my cradle bed,
And tears of sweet affection shed?
    My mother.

When pain and sickness made me cry,
Who gazed upon my heavy eye
And wept, for fear that I should die?
    My mother.

Who ran to help me when I fell
And would some pretty story tell,
Or kiss the part to make it well?
    My mother.

Who taught my infant lips to pray,
To love God's holy word and day,
And walk in wisdom's way?
    My mother.

And can I ever cease to be
Affectionate and kind to thee
Who wast so very kind to me,—
                    My mother.

Oh no, the thought I cannot bear;
And if God please my life to spare
I hope I shall reward thy care,
                    My mother.

When thou art feeble, old and gray,
My healthy arm shall be thy stay,
And I will soothe thy pains away,
                    My mother.

And when I see thee hang thy head,
'Twill be my turn to watch thy bed,
And tears of sweet affection shed,—
                    My mother.

When Mother Scrubs

New York Herald

WHEN mother scrubs us Sunday morn,
    There's lively times, you bet;
There's faces wry, with howl and cry
    To keep out of the wet.
There's argument and weak excuse
    And faces full forlorn
When mother scrubs and digs and rubs
    Us every Sunday morn.

When mother scrubs us, there's a glow
    Of white comes o'er the scene,

A shedding of the old and new,
  Comes where the old has been;
A shrinkage in more ways than one,
  A wish we'd never been born,
When mother scours with all her powers
  On every Sunday morn.

When mother scrubs us Sunday morn,
  She gets all out of breath;
She pants and sweats and sighs and frets
  And scrubs us 'most to death.
She scrubs our backs till they are sore,
  Till skin and flesh are gone,
Then wonders why we'd rather die
  Than wake on Sunday morn.

No wonder Billy Buzzey says
  That I'm a thin-skinned jay;
I've got to be, 'cuz ma, you see,
  Has scrubbed it all away.
Oh, won't we be a happy lot,
  The wildest ever born,
When we're too big for ma to dig
  And scrub on Sunday morn?

Which Loved Her Best?

Joy Allison

" I LOVE you, mother," said little John;
Then, forgetting his work, his cap went on,
And he was off to the garden swing,
Leaving his mother the wood to bring.

" I love you mother," said rosy Nell;
" I love you better than tongue can tell; "
Then she teased and pouted full half the day,
Till her mother rejoiced when she went to play.

" I love you, mother," said little Fan;
" To-day I'll help you all I can;
How glad I am that school doesn't keep! "
So she rocked the baby till it fell asleep.

Then, stepping softly, she took the broom,
And swept the floor, and dusted the room;
Busy and happy all day was she,
Helpful and cheerful as child could be.

" I love you, mother,'" again they said —
Three little children going to bed;
How do you think that mother guessed
Which of them really loved her best?

Mothers

Edwin L. Sabin

MOTHERS are the queerest things!
   'Member when John went away,
All but mother cried and cried
   When they said good-bye that day?
She just talked, and seemed to be
   Not the slightest bit upset —
Was the only one who smiled!
   Others' eyes were streaming wet.

But when John came back again
  On a furlough, safe and sound,
With a medal for his deeds,
  And without a single wound,
While the rest of us hurrahed,
  Laughed and joked and danced about,
Mother kissed him, then she cried —
  Cried and cried like all git out!

What is Home without a Mother?

Alice Hawthorne

WHAT is home without a mother?
  What are all the living joys we meet
When her loving smile no longer
  Greets the coming of our feet?
The days seem long, the nights seem drear,
  And time rolls slowly on,
And, oh! how few are childhood's pleasures
  When her gentle care is gone.

Things we prize are first to vanish,
  Hearts we love to pass away;
And how soon, e'en in our childhood,
  We behold her turning gray;
Her eye grows dim, her step is slow;
  Her joys of earth are past;
And sometimes ere we learn to know her,
  She hath breathed on earth her last.

Older hearts may have their sorrows,
  Griefs that quickly die away,
But a mother lost in childhood,
  Grieves the heart from day to day;

We miss her kind, her willing hand,
    Her fond and honest care;
And, oh, how dark is life around us!
    What is home without her care?

Tributes to Mother

Mothers' Day is a pretty idea which has taken root in many parts of our country and seems destined to grow. It was Miss Anna Jarvis of 2,031 North 12th St., Philadelphia, who suggested, two or three years ago, that the second Sunday in May be so designated, and that a white carnation be worn in honor of — Mother. Its observance on Sunday detracts not at all from business, religious observance, or pleasure. Let not the day pass without some kindly act or word for Mother or in her memory.

All I am or can be I owe to my angel Mother.— *Abraham Lincoln.*

God could not be everywhere, therefore He made Mothers. *Lew Wallace.*

What matter if the cheek show not the rose,
Nor eyes divine are there, nor queenly grace?
The Mother's glory lights the homely face.
                    — *Sir Lewis Morris.*

There was a place in childhood that I remember well,
And there a voice of sweetest tone bright fairy tales did tell.
                    — *Samuel Lover.*

Womanliness means only Motherhood,
All love begins and ends there.
                    — *Robert Browning.*

My Mother, when I learned that thou wast dead,
Say, wast thou conscious of the tears I shed?
Hovered thy spirit o'er the sorrowing son,

Wretched even then, life's journey just begun?
Perhaps thou gavest me, though unfelt, a kiss;
Perhaps a tear, if souls may weep in bliss
Ah, that maternal smile — it answers Yes!

> — *Cowper.*

A Mother is a Mother still,
The holiest thing alive.

> — *Coleridge.*

Who ran to help me when I fell,
And would some pretty story tell,
Or kiss the place to make it well?
My Mother

> — *Jane Taylor.*

Youth fades; love droops; the heavens of friendship fall;
A Mother's secret hope outlives them all.

> — *Oliver Wendell Holmes.*

In the Heavens above,
The angels whispering to one another
Can find among their burning terms of love
None so devotional as that of Mother.

> — *Edgar Allan Poe.*

For the hand that rocks the cradle rules the world.

> — *William Wallace.*

A kiss from my Mother made me a painter.

> — *Benjamin West.*

I have not wept these forty years; but now
My Mother comes afresh into my eyes.

> — *Dryden.*

The only love which on this teeming earth
Asks no return for passion's wayward birth.

> — *Hon. Mrs. Norton.*

A Mother's love — how sweet the name!
　What is a Mother's love?
A noble, pure, and tender flame,
　Enkindled from above.
To bless a heart of earthly mold;
The warmest love that can grow old,—
　This is Mother's love.
　　　　　　　　　　— F. Montgomery.

There is none, in all this cold and hollow world,
No fount of deep, strong, deathless love, save that within
A Mother's heart!
　　　　　　　　　　— Mrs. Hemans.

My Mother! Manhood's anxious brow
　And sterner cares have long been mine;
Yet turn I to thee fondly now,
　As when upon thy bosom's shrine
My infant griefs were gently hushed to rest,
And thy low whispered prayers my slumber blessed.
　　　　　　　　　　— George W. Bethune.

Absent many a year
Far o'er the sea, his sweetest dreams were still
Of that dear voice that soothed his infancy.
　　　　　　　　　　— Southey.

I miss thee, dear Mother, when young health has fled,
　And I sink in the languor of pain!
Where, where is the arm that once pillowed my head,
　And the ear that once heard me complain?

Other hands may support me, gentle accents may fall;
　For the fond and the true are still mine
I've a blessing for each; I am grateful to all;
　But whose care can be soothing as thine?
　　　　　　　　　　— Eliza Cook.

The Mother's love — there's none so pure,
  So constant and so kind;
No human passion doth endure
  Like this within the mind.

                  — Mrs. Hale.

There is not a grand inspiring thought,
There is not a truth by wisdom taught,
There is not a feeling pure and high,
That may not be read in a Mother's eye.

There are teachings in earth, and sky, and air,
The heavens the glory of God declare;
But louder than voice, beneath, above,
He is heard to speak through a Mother's love.

                  — Emily Taylor.

The loss of a Mother is always felt. Even though her health may incapacitate her from taking any active part in the care of her family, still she is a sweet rallying point, around which affection and obedience and a thousand tender endeavors to please, concentrate: and — dreary is the blank when such a point is withdrawn!

                  — Lemartine.

I see my Mother's calm, sad face,
  Look through the mist of bygone years,
And from yon high and holy place
  Her accents come into mine ears
  To bid me hope amid my fears.

                  — Egone.

The Mother in her office holds the key
Of the soul; and she it is who stamps the coin
Of character, and makes the being, who would be a savage
But for her gentle cares, a Christian man;
Then crown her Queen of the World!

                  — Old Play.

Let us, then, at the time appointed gather around their sacred remains and garland the passionless mounds above them with choicest flowers of springtime; let us raise above them the dear old flag they saved from dishonor; let us in this solemn presence renew our pledge to aid and assist those whom they have left among us, a sacred charge upon a nation's gratitude — the soldier's and sailor's widow and orphan.— *John A. Logan.*

MEMORIAL DAY

May 30

The 30th day of May was first designated in memory of our brave soldiers who fought to preserve the Union. John A. Logan, Commander-in-Chief of the Grand Army of the Republic, issued an order to that body in 1868 stating that that day would be set aside for the purpose of decorating the graves of those who were killed in the Civil War. All but nine states of the Union have made this day a legal holiday which is observed with parades and appropriate ceremonies not only in honor of those who fell in the Civil War but also in the World War and other conflicts.

Memorial Day

Was established by Commander-in-Chief John A. Logan, in the following General Order : —

Headquarters, Grand Army of the Republic,
Washington, D. C., May 5, 1868.
General Orders,
   No. II.

I. The 30th day of May, 1868, is designated for the purpose of strewing with flowers or otherwise decorating the graves of comrades who died in defence of their country during the late rebellion, and whose bodies now lie in almost every city, village and hamlet churchyard in the land. In this observance no form of ceremony is prescribed, but Posts and comrades will in their own way arrange such fitting services and testimonials of respect as circumstances may permit.

We are organized, comrades, as our Regulations tell us, for the purpose, among other things, " of preserving and strengthening those kind and fraternal feelings which have bound together the soldiers, sailors and marines who united to suppress the late rebellion." What can aid more to assure this result than by cherishing tenderly the memory of our heroic dead, who made their breasts a barricade between our country and its foes? Their soldier lives were the reveille of freedom to a race in chains, and their deaths the tattoo of rebellious tyranny in arms. We should guard their graves with sacred vigilance. All that the consecrated wealth and taste of the nation can add to their adornment and security is but a fitting tribute to the memory of her slain defenders. Let no wanton foot tread rudely on such hallowed grounds. Let pleasant paths invite the coming and going of reverent visitors and fond mourners. Let no vandalism of avarice or neglect, no ravages of time testify to the present or to the coming generations that we have forgotten as a people the cost of a free and undivided Republic.

If other eyes grow dull and other hands slack, and other hearts cold in the solemn trust, ours shall keep it well as long as the light and warmth of life remain to us.

Let us, then, at the time appointed gather around their sacred remains and garland the passionless mounds above them with choicest flowers of springtime; let us raise above them the dear old flag they saved from dishonor; let us in this solemn presence renew our pledges to aid and assist those whom they have left among us, a sacred charge upon a nation's gratitude — the soldier's and sailor's widow and orphan.

II. It is the purpose of the Commander-in-Chief to inaugurate this observance with the hope that it will be kept up from year to year while a survivor of the war remains to honor the memory of his departed comrades. He earnestly desires the public press to call attention to this Order, and lend its friendly aid in bringing it to the notice of comrades in all parts of the country in time for the simultaneous compliance therewith.

III. Department Commanders will use every effort to make this Order effective.

By command of

JOHN A. LOGAN, *Commander-in-Chief.*

N. P. CHIPMAN, *Adjutant-General.*

Memorial Day

Theodosia Garrison

A HANDFUL of old men walking down the village street
In worn, brushed uniforms, their grey heads high,—
A faded flag above them, one drum to lift their feet,
Look again, O, heart of mine, and see what passes by.

There's a vast crowd swaying, there's a wild band playing,
The streets are full of marching men, of tramping
cavalry,
Alive and young and straight again, they ride to greet a
mate again,—
The gallant souls, the great souls that live eternally.

A handful of old men walking down the highways?
Nay, we look on heroes that march among their peers,
The great, glad Companies have swung from Heaven's
byways
And come to join their own again across the dusty years.

There are strong hands meeting, there are staunch hearts
greeting,—
A crying of remembered names, of deeds that shall
not die.
A handful of old men? — Nay, my heart, look well again;
The spirit of America today is marching by!

The Veteran

Anonymous

EVERY year they're marching slower, every year they're
    stooping lower,
  Every year the lilting music stirs the hearts of older
    men,
Every year the flags above them seem to bend and bless
    and love them,
  As if craving for the future when they'll never march
    again.

Every year that day draws nearer, every year this truth
    is clearer,
  That the men who saved the nation from the severing
    Southern sword,
Soon must pass away forever from the scene of their en-
    deavor;
  Soon must answer to the roll-call of the Angel of the
    Lord.

Every year that dwindling number, loyal still to those that
    slumber,
  Forth they march to where already many have found
    peace at last;
And they place the fairest blossoms o'er the silent molder-
    ing blossoms,
  Of the valiant friends and comrades of the battles of
    the past.

Every year grow dimmer, duller, tattered flag and faded
    color,

Every year the hands that bear them find a harder task
    to do ;
And the eyes that only brighten when the blaze of battles
    lighten,
    Like the tattered flags they follow are grown dim and
    faded too.

Every year we see them massing, every year we watch
    them passing,
    Scarcely pausing in our hurry after they are off again ;
But the tattered flags above them seem to bend and bless
    and love them,
    And through all the lilting music sounds an undertone
    of pain.

Remembering Day

Mary Wight Saunders

ALL the soldiers marching along ;
All the children singing a song ;
All the flowers dewy and sweet ;
All the flags hung out in the street ;
Hearts that throb in a grateful way —
For this is our Remembering Day.

The Blue and the Gray

Francis Miles Finch

BY the flow of the inland river,
    Whence the fleets of iron have fled,
Where the blades of the grave-grass quiver,
    Asleep are the ranks of the dead :

Under the sod and the dew,
　Waiting the judgment day;
Under the one, the Blue,
　Under the other, the Gray.

These in the robings of glory,
　Those in the gloom of defeat,
All with the battle-blood gory,
　In the dusk of eternity meet:
　Under the sod and the dew,
　　Waiting the judgment day;
　Under the laurel, the Blue,
　　Under the willow, the Gray.

From the silence of sorrowful hours
　The desolate mourners go,
Lovingly laden with flowers
　Alike for the friend and the foe:
　Under the sod and the dew,
　　Waiting the judgment day;
　Under the roses, the Blue,
　　Under the lilies, the Gray.

So, with an equal splendor,
　The morning sun-rays fall,
With a touch impartially tender,
　On the blossoms blooming for all;
　Under the sod and the dew,
　　Waiting the judgment day;
　Broidered with gold, the Blue,
　　Mellowed with gold, the Gray.

No more shall the war-cry sever,
　Or the winding rivers be red;

They banish our anger forever
 When they laurel the graves of our dead!
   Under the sod and the dew,
     Waiting the judgment day;
   Love and tears for the Blue,
     Tears and love for the Gray.

A Knot of Blue and Gray

Anonymous

You ask me why, upon my breast,
  Unchanged from day to day,
Linked side by side in this broad band,
  I wear the blue and gray.
I had two brothers long ago,—
  Two brothers, blithe and gay;
One wore a suit of Northern blue,
  And one a suit of Southern gray.
One heard the roll-call of the South,
  And linked his fate with Lee;
The other bore the Stars and Stripes
  With Sherman to the sea.

Each fought for what he deemed was right,
  And fell with sword in hand;
One sleeps amid Virginia's hills,
  And one by Georgia's strand,
But the same sun shines on both their graves,
  'Mid valley and o'er hill,
And in the darkest of the hours
  My brothers do live still.
And this is why, upon my breast,
  Unchanged from day to day,

Linked side by side in this broad band,
I wear a knot of blue and gray.

Cheers for the Living — Tears for the Dead!

Robert G. Ingersoll

THE past rises before me like a dream. Again we are
in the great struggle for national life. We hear the
sounds of preparation — the music of boisterous drums
— the silver voices of heroic bugles. We see thousands
of assemblages, and hear the appeals of orators; we see
the pale cheeks of women and the flushed faces of men;
and in those assemblages we see all the dead whose dust
we have covered deep with flowers.

We lose sight of them no more. We are with them
when they enlist in the great army of freedom. We see
them part with those they love. Some are walking for
the last time in quiet, woody places with the maidens they
adore. We hear the whisperings and the sweet vows of
eternal love as they lingeringly part forever. Others are
bending over cradles, kissing babes that are asleep. Some
are receiving the blessings of old men. Some are parting
with mothers who hold them and press them to their
hearts again and again, and say nothing. Kisses and tears,
tears and kisses — divine mingling of agony and love!
And some are talking with wives and endeavoring with
brave words, spoken in the old tones, to drive from their
hearts the awful fear. We see them part. We see the
wife standing in the door with the babe in her arms —
standing in the sunlight sobbing — at the turn of the road
a hand waves — she answers by holding high in her loving arms the child. He is gone, and forever.

We see them all as they march proudly away and under

the flaunting flags, keeping time to the grand, wild music of war — marching down the streets of the great cities — through the towns and across the prairies — down to the fields of glory, to do and to die for the eternal right.

We go with them, one and all. We are by their side on the gory fields — in all the hospitals of pain — on all the weary marches. We stand guard with them in the wild storm and under the quiet stars. We are with them in ravines running with blood — in the furrows of old fields. We are with them between contending hosts, unable to move, wild with thirst, the life ebbing slowly away among the withered leaves. We see them pierced by balls and torn with shells, in the trenches, by forts, and in the whirlwind of the charge, where men become iron, with nerves of steel.

They sleep beneath the shadows of the clouds, careless alike of sunshine or of storm, each in the windowless palace of Rest. Earth may run red with other wars — they are at peace. In the midst of battle, in the roar of conflict, they found the serenity of death. I have one sentiment for soldiers living and dead: Cheers for the living; tears for the dead.

I Have a Son

Emory Pottle

I HAVE a son who goes to France
To-morrow.
I have clasped his hand —
Most men will understand —
And wished him, smiling, lucky chance in France.
My son!
At last the house is still —

Just the dog and I in the garden — dark —
Stars and my pipe's red spark —
The house his young heart used to fill
Is still.

He said one day, " I've got to go
To France — Dad, you know how I feel! "
I knew.   Like sun and steel
And morning.   " Yes," I said, " I know
You'll go."

I'd waited just to hear him speak
Like that.
God, what if I had had
Another sort of lad,
Something too soft and meek and weak
To speak!

And yet!
He could not guess the blow
He'd struck.
Why, he's my only son!
And we had just begun
To be dear friends.   But I dared not show
The blow.

But now — to-night —
No, no; it's right;
I never had a righter thing
To bear.   And men must fling
Themselves away in the grieving sight
Of right.

A handsome boy — but I, who knew
His spirit — well, they cannot mar
The cleanness of a star
That'll shine to me, always and true,
Who knew.

I've given him,
Yes; and had I more,
I'd give them too — for there's a love
That asking, asks above
The human measure of our store —
And more.

Yes; it hurts!
Here in the dark, alone —
No one to see my wet old eyes —
I'll watch the morning rise —
And only God shall hear my groan
Alone.

I have a son who goes to France
To-morrow.
I have clasped his hand —
Most men will understand —
And wished him, smiling, lucky chance
In France.

In Flanders Fields

Lieut. Col. John D. McCrae

In Flanders fields the poppies blow
Between the crosses, row on row,
That mark our place; and in the sky
The larks, still bravely singing, fly,
Scarce heard amidst the guns below.
We are the dead. Short days ago
We loved, felt dawn, saw sunset glow,
Lived and were loved, and now we lie
 In Flanders fields.

Take up our quarrel with the foe!
To you from falling hands we throw
The torch. Be yours to hold it high!
If ye break faith with us who die
We shall not sleep, though poppies grow
 In Flanders fields.

America's Answer

R. W. Lillard

Rest ye in peace, ye Flanders dead.
The fight that ye so bravely led
We've taken up. And we will keep
True faith with you who lie asleep
With each a cross to mark his bed,
And poppies blowing overhead,
Where once his own life blood ran red.
So let your rest be sweet and deep
 In Flanders fields.

Fear not that ye have died for naught.
The torch ye threw to us we caught.
Ten million hands will hold it high,
And Freedom's light shall never die!
We've learned the lesson that ye taught
In Flanders fields.

Crosses

Mabel Hicks

THE moon shines down on Flanders' Fields
　On crosses white and bare,
But One who watches over them
　A crown of thorns did wear.

They do not sleep alone, our boys,
　For angels day and night
He giveth charge to watch and keep
　Them ever in their sight.

So not forgotten shall they be,
　Who died that we might live,
Who gladly gave their lives for us —
　Gave all they had to give.

The moon still shines on Flanders' Fields,
　On crosses white as snow,
But whiter are the souls of those
　Whom God and Christ doth know.

For, mothers, all your boys are there,
　He gathered them all in;
And safe within the fold they are,
　Cleansed each from every sin.

For He who gave His only Son
   Can surely understand
That they laid down their lives for us,
   And for their native land.

Oh! moon, shine on in Flanders' Fields
   And touch each cross with peace;
And let them quietly sleep on
   Whose souls have found release.

Saint Jeanne

Theodosia Garrison

There is a little church in France to-day
   Where once a simple maiden knelt, who now
   Wears God's insignia upon her brow —
First of all the saints to whom her people pray.
Maid of the Lilies, warrior of the Sword,
     Jeanne d'Arc,
True soldier in the service of the Lord,
     Shall you not hark?

To-day the candles burn before your shrine,
   Your banner glows within the sacred space,
   But not alone, for with it, by God's grace,
There does another of its color shine;
Two and yet one — a holy thing enshrined,
     Sainte Jeanne,
Two banners at Domremy are entwined,
     Bless them as one.

There is a little church in France to-day;
   How many prayers have risen thence to you!
   For their sake heed another prayer and new,

Strange words yet beautiful your people say.
Bend down between the lilies and the lance,
    Sainte Jeanne.
" For those Americans who died for France "
    Light their souls on!

There is a little church in France to-day;
    Your people kneel about the altar there.
    You who were warrior and woman, hear
With hands of very love this prayer they pray:
A simple prayer for those souls chivalrous
    Who dared the dark,
" For those Americans who died for us,"
    Jeanne d'Arc.

Memorial Day — To-day

Anonymous

THE observance of a day of sacred memory indicates
how real and vital is the religious feeling of the American people, and how it is possible in the most tender
mood to feel ourselves united. Patriotism, in its higher
ranges, is woven of the same fabric as religion.

The most sacred service of Christianity — that which
amid all change has endured, has been a memorial service. As Americans we have a memorial service in which
all the people come together, as members of a great family, to honor those who have gone before and in gratitude
for what they were and for what they achieved. It is a
solemn service, because it is in memory of sacrifice.

But the crown of sorrows is not in memory but in
forgetfulness. To forget our heroes would be the sad-
dest thing imaginable, and the American people have
resolved that the memory of those who fought at Gettys-

burg and Shiloh, at Château-Thierry and in the Argonne shall not be forgotten. Memorial Day to Americans now is no impersonal affair, but sacred with personal ties that reach across continents and oceans.

Great events that are recent and significant bring the meaning of the day close to every heart and home, and make it richer for this very fact. History that is read out of books is bound to be more or less ancient history to the reader, but history for the past few years has been intimate and vital, because it has been in the making and those close to us have taken part.

The true soldier stands before us as a martyr to a peace that must rest upon righteousness. The chastisement of society's sins is upon him. No period in our Nation's history shines with more refulgence than our Civil War period, in which men took upon themselves not only the sword but the cross. And the boys in the late war proved worthy of their sires and gave their lives to vindicate justice and to secure the perpetuity of liberty under law. To the men in blue and to their sons in khaki war was the test of sincerity and patriotism, and freely they gave witness to their faith in citizen sovereignty.

They did this without thought of reward. The man who gives his services and thinks of reward does not belong in this noble company of heroes, for they offered all without a thought of recompense. They were ready to be forgotten, if that for which they fought might be remembered. This element of personal sacrifice and unconcern constitutes their greatest glory. Through their sacrifices the Nation has become a sacred thing, and patriotism has taken on a new and higher meaning. What the heroes of '64 and '17 did ennobles all labor, all service, all sacrifice.

Tributes to America's Dead in the World War

WE pay silent and grateful tribute to-day to those gallant sons of America who have given their lives that the great principles of liberty and justice might endure. Their heroism, their love of country and their self-sacrifice, will forever constitute the brightest pages of American History. The traditions received from their forefathers gave them the inspiration for patriotic service which will be a consecrated guide for future generations. We shall always remember the brave soldiers of our Allies whose supreme sacrifice on the battlefields of Europe in the cause of right made victory possible. We salute the Allied dead.

John J. Pershing

Commander-in-Chief of the
American Expeditionary Forces.

ON the day on which America is mourning her brave dead, the thoughts of British soldiers who fought beside them will turn to her in sympathy for the bereaved, and in admiration and gratitude for her brave sons who gave their lives for our common cause. The knowledge that British and American soldiers shared the same hardships in the field, faced the same dangers and achieved a common victory for the same ideals must always be a strong bond of union between our two nations.

Haig

Field Marshal of the British Forces.

Les soldats Américains ont lutté côte à côte avec les soldats Français pour le triomphe de la Justice et du Droit.

Le sacrifice de ceux qui sont tombés nous trace le devoir, car leur voix s'élève sans cesse pour proclamer que, seule, l'union des pays alliés, scellée sur les champs de bataille, maintiendra la paix du monde.

[signature]

Commander-in-Chief of the Allied Forces.

Translation

The Americans fought side by side with the French soldiers for the triumph of Justice and Right.

The sacrifices of those who fell show clearly to us our duty, for their voices rise unceasingly to proclaim that only the union of the allied countries, sealed upon the fields of battle, will uphold the peace of the world.

Hymn to the Victorious Dead

Hermann Hagedorn

God, by the sea, by the resounding sea,
  God, in the vales, God, on the golden plain,
God, in the dark of cities, tremblingly
  We raise our hands, we raise our hearts, to Thee.
Our Spirits, Father, see, we raise to Thee
  In longing, Lord, in pain!

God, by the sea, more terrible than guns,
  God, on the hills, low-bending, oh, Divine,
We offer Thee our bright, beloved ones.
  In love, in grief, in pride, we yield our sons,
In Thy strong hands, Father, we lay our sons,
  No longer ours, but Thine.

God, through the night, the dark, tempestuous,
  See, with clear eyes we wait the day to be.
We do not ask that they come back to us.
  We know that, soon or late, victorious,
Even though they die, they will come back to us,
  Because they died for Thee!

Copyright 1918, by *The Outlook Co.*

The Debt

Theodosia Garrison

FOR THE YOUTH THEY GAVE AND THE BLOOD THEY GAVE,
FOR THE STRENGTH THAT WAS OUR STAY,
FOR EVERY MARKED OR NAMELESS GRAVE
ON THE STEEL-TORN FLANDERS WAY —
WE WHO ARE WHOLE OF BODY AND SOUL,
WE HAVE A DEBT TO PAY.

When we have justly given back again
To the maimed body and bewildered brain,
New strength and light and will to take one's part
In the world's work at field or desk or mart,
When this old joy of living we restore,
We shall have paid a little of our score.

When we have given to earth's stricken lands
The service of our minds and hearts and hands,
When we have made the blackened orchards bright,
And brought the homeless ones to warmth and light,
When we have made these desolate forget,
We shall have paid a little of our debt.

For the youth they gave and the blood they gave
We must render back the due;
For every marked or nameless grave
We must pay with a service true;
Till the scales stand straight with even weight
And the world is a world made new.

We Shall Remember Them

James Terry White

They sleep beneath no immemorial yews;
  Their resting place no temple arches hem;
No blazoned shaft or graven tablet woos
  Men's praise — and yet, we shall remember them.

The unforgetting clouds shall drop their tears;
  The winds in ceaseless lamentation, wail,
For God's white Knights are lying on their biers,
  Who vowed their service to restore the Grail.

They gave their lives to make the whole world free;
  They recked not to what flag they were assigned,
The Starry Banner, Cross, or Fleur-de-lis —
  Their sacrifice was made for all mankind.

For them the task is done, the strife is stilled;
  No more shall care disturb nor zeal condemn;

And when the larger good has been fulfilled,
  In coming years we shall remember them.

How can the world their deeds forget?   In France
  White crosses everywhere lift pallid hands,
Like silent sentinels with sword and lance,
  To keep their memory safe for other lands.

What need have they for holy sepulture?
  Within the hearts of men is hallowed ground —
A sanctuary where they rest secure,
  And with Love's immortality are crowned.

And far-off voices of the future sing,
  " They shall remain in memory's diadem ";
And winds of promise still are whispering
  Through storied years, " We shall remember them."

From *A Garden of Remembrance.*

Their Victory Won

Florence Earle Coates

WAN-VISAGED Azrael, in a darkened room,
  'Mid stifled sobs and pleadings full of fear,
I first was made to know thy presence drear;
And I supposed thee dweller of a tomb
Where quickly fade all fairest things that bloom:
  All loves, ambitions, dreams, that men hold dear.
  But now, O Death, beholding thee more near,
How changed thy look! how glorified thy gloom!

In the wide Open, 'neath a summer sky,
Bending above thy chosen, where they lie
    Upon the hard-won fields of Victory,
This have they taught me — these so young, so brave,
Who smiling gave their all, the world to save —
    Life is not lovelier than death may be!

From *Harper's Magazine.*

A Song for Heroes

Edwin Markham

(Author of "The Man with the Hoe and Other Poems.")

I

A SONG for the heroes who saw the sign
And took their place in the battle line;
They were walls of granite and gates of brass;
And they cried out to God, "They shall not pass!"
And they hurled them back in a storm of cheers,
And the sound will echo on over the years.

And a song for the end, the glorious end,
And the soldiers marching up over the bend
Of the broken roads in gallant France,
The homing heroes who took the chance,
Who looked on life, and with even breath
Faced the winds from the gulfs of death.
Their hearts are running on over the graves —
Over the battle-wrecks — over the waves —
Over the scarred fields — over the foam —
On to America — on to home!

II

And a song for the others, the heroes slain
In Argonne Forest — in St. Gobain —
In the flowery meadows of Picardy —
In Belgium — in Italy,
From brave Montello to the sea.

A song for the heroes gone on ahead
To join the hosts of the marching dead —
A song for the souls that could lightly fling
Sweet life away as a little thing
For the sake of the mighty need of earth,
The need of the ages coming to birth.

All praise to the daring God who gave
Heroic souls who could dare the grave.
Praise for the power He laid on youth
To challenge disaster and die for truth.
What greater gift can the High God give,
Than the power to die that the truth may live!

Glory to the Lord, the Hero of Heaven,
He whose wounds in His side are seven —
Glory that He gathers the heroes home,
Out of the red fields — out of the foam —
Gathers them out of the Everywhere,
Into the Camp that is Over There!

The New Banner

Katrina Trask

O FELLOW-CITIZENS of storm-tossed Lands,
  War weary! Sound the bugle-note! Arise!
New steadfast standards wait your eager hands,
  The Star of Promise orbs to meet your eyes.
    Great Kings must pass, that mankind may be free,
    Beneath the banner of Democracy!

The Mighty Ruler of this mortal life
  Has wisdom, not by mortals understood:
The seeds of blood, the deeds of wanton strife
  Shall some day harvest unexpected good.
    Great Kings shall pass and every nation be
    Ruled by the people — for the people, free.

When the mad anguish of this stricken world —
  Where valiant heroes daily fight and fall —
Has passed and Freedom's banners are unfurled,
  Then shall we know the reason for it all!
    Then every waiting, heart-sick land shall see
    The ultimate design of Destiny!

Brave men and women, laboring in toil —
  Who, faithful, fight with willing sword or pen,
Who work to break the rock or till the soil —
  Shall wear the high insignia of men.
    All kings must pass, that every man may be
    A monarch in his manhood, strong and free!

Beyond the present, unimagined woe,
  A glorious Day is breaking o'er the earth:

As Spring flowers blossom, after ice-bound snow,
The God of Gods shall bring new things to birth.
It is the dawn! Great forces are set free!
All hail the Day! World-wide Democracy!

Quotations for Memorial Day

Let little hands bring blossoms sweet,
To brave men lying low;
Let little hearts to soldiers dead
Their love and honor show.
We'll love the flag they loved so well,
The dear old banner bright,
We'll love the land for which they fell,
With soul, and strength, and might!
— *S. M. Kneil.*

We'll honor the graves of our soldier dead,
Who heard their country's cry,
Who left their homes, and fought and bled
And died for liberty.

We'll bring them to-day the violets blue,
And roses red and white,
Those colors bright they bore so true,
For God and home and right.
— *Ada Simpson Sherwood.*

He who plows and plants that others may reap is of
noble blood; but he who dies that a nation may live is made
of the stern stuff that justifies the songs that sing his deeds
and the wreathed marble that marks the sacred spot where
his ashes sleep.— *Selected.*

Every mountain and hill shall have its treasured name,
every river shall keep some solemn title, every valley and
every lake shall cherish its honored register; and till the

mountains are worn out and the rivers forget to flow, till the clouds are weary of replenishing springs, and the springs forget to gush, and the rills to sing, shall their names be kept fresh with reverent honors which are inscribed upon the book of National Remembrance.— *Henry Ward Beecher.*

> Sleep, soldiers! still in honored rest
> Your truth and valor wearing;
> The bravest are the tenderest —
> The loving are the daring.
>
> — *Bayard Taylor.*

The light that shines from a patriot's grave is a pure and holy light.— *Homer Everett.*

I invoke all who heed well the lesson of Decoration Day, to weave each year a fresh garland for the grave of some hero and to rebuke any and all who talk of civil war, save as the " last dread tribunal of kings and peoples."— *Gen. Wm. L. Sherman.*

In the field of Gettysburg, as we now behold it, the blue and the gray blending in happy harmony, like the mingling hues of the summer landscape, we may see the radiant symbol of the triumphant America of our pride, our hope and our joy.— *George William Curtis.*

Those who fought against us are now of us and with us reverently acknowledge that above all the desires of men move the majestic laws of God, evolving alike from victory or defeat of nations, a substantial good for all his children.— *Gen. George A. Sheridan.*

By the homely traditions of the fireside, by the headstones in the churchyard consecrated to those whose forms repose far off in rude graves, or sleep beneath the sea, embalmed in the memory of succeeding generations of parents and children, the heroic dead will live on in immortal youth.— *Gov. Andrew of Massachusetts.*

> The Northern lights are blending
> With the rays of the Southern Cross,
> And the gulf is bridged between them
> By a common sense of loss.
> — *Susan J. Adams.*

So long as the glorious flag for which they died waves over our reunited country, will each recurring spring see fresh laurels on the graves of our country's dead.— *Anonymous.*

Why mourn for those who slumber here? Their epitaphs are written in the grandest history of the ages. Before them will reverently pass the procession of the centuries. And every headstone roundabout, even those without a name, will be given honorable place in the mighty monument that is to commemorate the ennobling and uplifting of the human race.— *Anonymous.*

> Sleep, comrades! sleep and rest
> On this field of grounded arms,
> Where foes no more molest,
> Nor sentry's shot alarms.

> Stoop, angels, hither from the skies!
> There is no holier spot of ground
> Than where defeated valor lies
> By mourning beauty crowned.
> — *Henry Wadsworth Longfellow.*

These heroes are dead. They died for liberty — they died for us. They are at rest. They sleep in the land they made free, under the flag they rendered stainless, under the solemn pines, the sad hemlocks, the tearful willows, and the embracing vines. They sleep beneath the shadows of the clouds, careless alike of the sunshine or of storm, each in the windowless palace of rest. Earth may run red with other wars — they are at peace. In the midst of battle, in the roar of conflict, they found the serenity of death. I have one sentiment for the soldiers, living and dead — cheers for the living and tears for the dead.— *Robert G. Ingersoll.*

> The muffled drum's sad roll has beat
>   The soldier's last tattoo;
> No more on Life's parade shall meet
>   That brave and fallen few.
> On Fame's eternal camping ground,
>   Their silent tents are spread,
> And glory guards, with solemn round,
>   The bivouac of the dead.
> — *Theodore O'Hara.*

Let our children know the names and deeds of the men who preserved the Union; let piety and patriotism sweetly unite in forming the character of our children, that we may have a race of loyal and noble Americans to carry forward the triumphs of liberty after those who won it have gone to their reward.— *Robert S. MacArthur.*

Oh, tell me not that they are dead,— that generous host, that airy army of invisible heroes. They hover as a cloud of witnesses above this nation. Are they dead that yet speak, louder than we can speak, and a more universal language? Are they dead that yet act? Are they dead that yet move upon society, and inspire the people with nobler motives and more heroic patriotism.— *Henry Ward Beecher.*

> They sleep in their manhood, the true and the brave,
> And Liberty guardeth each patriot's grave;
> Some in the sunlight, and some in the shade,
> Some 'neath the vine in the wren-haunted glade,
> Some in a nook nearly hidden from sight,
> Others far upon the lone mountain height;
> Though scattered they be, the Blue and the Gray,
> The love of the Nation will find them to-day.
> — *T. C. Harbaugh.*

Strew loving offerings o'er the brave,
Their country's joy, their country's pride;
For us their precious lives they gave,
For Freedom's sacred cause they died.
— *S. F. Smith.*

Your silent tents of green
    We deck with fragrant flowers;
Yours has the suffering been,
    The memory shall be ours.
— *Henry Wadsworth Longfellow.*

'Twas not in vain, O noble band,
    Your blood imbued Columbia's sod,
United now her children stand,—
    One flag, one country and one God.
— *George D. Emery.*

The hundreds of thousands who fell on both sides did not die in vain. The power, the divine power, which made for us a garden of swords, sowing the land broadcast with sorrow, will reap thence for us, and for the ages, a nation truly divine; a nation of freedom and of free men; where tolerance shall walk hand in hand with religion, while civilization points out to patriotism the many open highways to human right and glory.— *Henry Watterson.*

FLAG DAY

June 14

This day was first recognized June 14, 1894, when the Governor of New York ordered the Stars and Stripes to be raised on all public buildings in the state. June 14th is the anniversary of the adoption of the Stars and Stripes by the Continental Congress at Philadelphia in the year 1777.

The Story of Our Flag

Alfred P. Putnam

THE history of our flag is of very great interest, and
brings to memory many sacred and thrilling associations.
The banner of St. Andrew was blue, charged with a white
saltier or cross, in the form of the letter X. It was used
in Scotland as early as the eleventh century. The banner of St. George was white, charged with a red cross;
and it was used in England as early as the first part of
the fourteenth century. By a royal proclamation, dated
April 22, 1700, two crosses were joined together upon
the same banner.

This ancient banner of England suggested the basis of
our own flag. Other flags had been used at different
times by our colonial ancestors, but they were not associated with, or made a part of, the " Stars and Stripes."

It was after Washington had taken command of the
Revolutionary army at Cambridge, in 1776, that he un-
folded before them the flag of thirteen stripes of alternate red and white, having upon one of its corners the
red and white crosses of St. George and St. Andrew on
a field of blue. This was the standard which was borne
into Boston when it was evacuated by the British troops
and was entered by the American army.

Uniting, as it did, the flags of England and America,
it showed that the colonists had not yet decided to sever
the tie that bound them to the mother country. By that
union of flags it was signified that the colonies were still

a substantial part of the British Empire, and that they demanded the rights which such a relation implied. On the other hand, the thirteen stripes represented the union of the thirteen colonies; the white stripes indicated the purity of their cause, the red declared their defiance of cruelty and persecution.

On the 14th of June, 1777, it was resolved by Congress, " That the flag of the thirteen United States be thirteen stripes, alternate red and white, and that the union be thirteen white stars in a blue field." This resolution was made public in September, 1777, and the flag that was first made and used in pursuance of it was that which led the Americans to victory at Saratoga. The stars were arranged in a circle, in order, perhaps, to express the equality of the states.

In 1794, there having been two more new states added to the Union, it was voted that the alternate stripes, as well as the stars, be fifteen in number. The flag thus altered and enlarged was the banner borne through all the contests of the War of 1812. It was observed, however, that if a new stripe should be added with every freshly admitted state, the flag would at length become inconveniently large. In 1818, therefore, Congress enacted that a permanent return should be made to the original number of thirteen stripes, and that the number of stars should be increased to correspond with the number of states.

Thus the flag might symbolize the Union as it might be at any given period of its history, and also as it was at the time of its birth. It was at the same time suggested that the stars, instead of being arranged in a circle, be formed into a single star — a suggestion which was occasionally adopted. At the present time it is sufficient if all the stars are there upon that azure field — the blue to be emblematical of perseverance, vigilance, and justice, and each star to signify the glory of the state it may represent.

What precious associations cluster around our flag!

Where has it not gone, the pride of its friends and the terror of its foes? What countries and what seas has it not visited? Where has not the American citizen been able to stand beneath its guardian folds and defy the world? With what joy and exultation seamen and travelers have gazed upon its stars and stripes, read in it the history of their nation's glory, and drawn from it the inspirations of patriotism!

Our Flag

Margaret E. Sangster

FLAG of the fearless-hearted,
  Flag of the broken chain,
Flag in a day-dawn started,
  Never to pale or wane.
Dearly we prize its colors,
  With the heaven light breaking through,
The clustered stars and the steadfast bars,
  The red, the white, and the blue.

Flag of the sturdy fathers,
  Flag of the loyal sons,
Beneath its folds it gathers
  Earth's best and noblest ones.
Boldly we wave its colors,
  Our veins are thrilled anew
By the steadfast bars, the clustered stars,
  The red, the white, and the blue.

The Star-Spangled Banner

Francis Scott Key

OH ! say can you see, by the dawn's early light,
   What so proudly we hailed at the twilight's last gleam-
     ing ;
Whose broad stripes and bright stars through the perilous
   fight,
   O'er the ramparts we watched, were so gallantly
     streaming?
And the rocket's red glare, the bombs bursting in air,
Gave proof through the night that our flag was still
   there ;
   Oh, say, does that star-spangled banner yet wave
O'er the land of the free and the home of the brave?

On the shore, dimly seen through the mists of the deep,
   Where the foe's haughty host in dread silence reposes,
What is that which the breeze o'er the towering steep
   As it fitfully blows, half conceals, half discloses?
Now it catches the gleam of the morning's first beam;
In full glory reflected now shines on the stream;
   'T is the star-spangled banner ! Oh ! long may it wave
   O'er the land of the free and the home of the brave !

And where is the band who so vauntingly swore,
   Mid the havoc of war and the battle's confusion,
A home and a country they'd leave us no more?
   Their blood hath washed out their foul footsteps' pol-
     lution ;
No refuge could save the hireling and slave
From the terror of flight, or the gloom of the grave,

And the star-spangled banner in triumph doth wave
O'er the land of the free and the home of the brave.

Oh! thus be it ever, when freemen shall stand
Between their loved home and the war's desolation;
Blessed with victory and peace, may the Heaven-rescued
land
Praise the Power that hath made and preserved us a
nation.
Then conquer we must, for our cause it is just,
And this be our our motto, " In God is our trust ":
And the star-spangled banner in triumph shall wave
O'er the land of the free and the home of the brave.

The New Pledge to the Flag

I Pledge allegiance to the Flag of the United States of
America and to the Republic for which it stands,
One nation, indivisible, with liberty and justice for all.

A Creed

Edgar A. Guest

Lord, let me not in service lag,
Let me be worthy of our flag;
Let me remember, when I'm tried,
The sons heroic who have died
In freedom's name, and in my way
Teach me to be as brave as they.

In all I am, in all I do
Unto our flag I would be true;
For God and country let me stand.
Unstained of soul and clean of hand,

Teach me to serve and guard and love
The Starry Flag which flies above.

By permission of the Reilly & Lee Co., Chicago.

The Unfurling of the Flag

Clara Endicott Sears

THERE'S a streak across the skyline
  That is gleaming in the sun,
Watchers from the lighthouse towers
Signalled it to foreign Powers
  Just as daylight had begun,
    Message thrilling,
    Hopes fulfilling
To those fighting o'er the seas.
" It's the flag we've named Old Glory
That's unfurling to the breeze."

Can you see the flashing emblem
  Of our Country's high ideal?
Keep your lifted eyes upon it
And draw joy and courage from it,
  For it stands for what is real,
    Freedom's calling
    To the falling
From oppression's hard decrees.
It's the flag we've named Old Glory
You see floating in the breeze.

Glorious flag we raise so proudly,
  Stars and stripes, red, white and blue,
You have been the inspiration
Of an ever growing nation

Such as this world never knew.
    Peace and Justice,
    Freedom, Progress,
Are the blessings we can seize
When the flag we call Old Glory
Is unfurling to the breeze.

When the cry of battling nations
    Reaches us across the space
Of the wild tumultuous ocean,
Hearts are stirred with deep emotion
    For the saving of the race!
    Peace foregoing,
    Aid bestowing,
First we drop on bended knees,
Then with shouts our grand Old Glory
We set flaunting to the breeze!

The Flag Goes By

Henry Holcomb Bennett

HATS off!
Along the street there comes
A blare of bugles, a ruffle of drums,
A flash of color beneath the sky:
    Hats off!
The flag is passing by!

Blue and crimson and white it shines
Over the steel-tipped, ordered lines.
    Hats off!
The colors before us fly;
But more than the flag is passing by.

Sea-fights and land-fights, grim and great,
Fought to make and to save the State:
Weary marches and sinking ships;
Cheers of victory on dying lips;

Days of plenty and years of peace;
March of a strong land's swift increase;
Equal justice, right, and law,
Stately honor and reverend awe;

Sign of a nation, great and strong
To ward her people from foreign wrong:
Pride and glory and honor,— all
Live in the colors to stand or fall.

    Hats off!
Along the street there comes
A blare of bugles, a ruffle of drums;
And loyal hearts are beating high:
    Hats off!
The flag is passing by!

Your Flag and My Flag

Wilbur D. Nesbit

Your flag and my flag,
  And how it flies to-day
In your land and my land
  And half a world away!
Rose-red and blood-red
  The stripes forever gleam;
Snow-white and soul-white
  The good forefathers' dream;

Sky-blue and true-blue with stars to gleam aright —
The glorified guidon of the day; a shelter through the
    night.

      Your flag and my flag!
        To every star and stripe
      The drums beat as hearts beat
        And fifers shrilly pipe!
      Your flag and my flag —
        A blessing in the sky;
      Your hope and my hope —
        It never hid a lie!
Home land and far land and half the world around —
Old Glory hears our glad salute and ripples to the
    sound.

      Your flag and my flag!
        And, oh, how much it holds —
      Your land and my land —
        Secure within its folds!
      Your heart and my heart
        Beat quicker at the sight;
      Sun-kissed and wind-tossed —
        Red and blue and white.
The one flag — the great flag — the flag for me and
    you —
Glorified all else beside — the red and white and blue!

Stand By the Flag

John Nichols Wilder

STAND by the flag! On land and ocean billow
　By it your fathers stood unmoved and true,
Living, defended — dying, from their pillow,
　With their last blessing, passed it on to you.

Stand by the flag, all doubt and treason scorning!
　Believe with courage firm, and faith sublime,
That it will float, until the eternal morning
　Pales in its glories all the lights of Time!

Makers of the Flag

Franklin K. Lane

NOTE: The following address was delivered by the Honorable Franklin K. Lane, Secretary of the Interior, before the officers and employees of the Department, about 5,000 in number, at the Inner Court, Patent Office Building, June 14, 1914.

THIS morning, as I passed into the Land Office, The Flag dropped me a most cordial salutation, and from its rippling folds I heard it say: " Good morning, Mr. Flag Maker."

" I beg your pardon, Old Glory," I said, " aren't you mistaken? I am not the President of the United States, nor a member of Congress, nor even a general in the army. I am only a government clerk."

" I greet you again, Mr. Flag Maker," replied the gay voice, " I know you well. You are the man who worked in the swelter of yesterday straightening out the tangle of that farmer's homestead in Idaho, or perhaps you found the mistake in that Indian contract in Oklahoma, or helped to clear that patent for the hopeful inventor in New York, or pushed the opening of that new ditch in Colorado, or made that mine in Illinois more safe, or brought relief to the old soldier in Wyoming. No matter; whichever one of these beneficent individuals you may happen to be, I give you greeting, Mr. Flag Maker."

I was about to pass on, when the Flag stopped me with these words:

"Yesterday the president spoke a word that made happier the future of ten million peons in Mexico; but that act looms no larger on the flag than the struggle which the boy in Georgia is making to win the Corn Club prize this summer.

"Yesterday the Congress spoke a word which will open the door of Alaska; but a mother in Michigan worked from sunrise until far into the night, to give her boy an education. She, too, is making the flag.

"Yesterday we made a new law to prevent financial panics, and yesterday, maybe, a school teacher in Ohio taught his first letters to a boy who will one day write a song that will give cheer to the millions of our race. We are all making the flag."

"But," I said impatiently, "these people were only working."

Then came a great shout from The Flag:

"THE WORK that we do is the making of the flag.

"I am not the flag; not at all. I am but its shadow.

"I am whatever you make me, nothing more.

"I am your belief in yourself, your dream of what a people may become.

"I live a changing life, a life of moods and passions, of heartbreaks and tired muscles.

" Sometimes I am strong with pride, when men do an honest work, fitting the rails together truly.

" Sometimes I droop, for then purpose has gone from me, and cynically I play the coward.

" Sometimes I am loud, garish and full of that ego that blasts judgment.

" But always I am all that you hope to be, and have the courage to try for.

" I am song and fear, struggle and panic, and ennobling hope.

" I am the day's work of the weakest man, and the largest dream of the most daring.

" I am the Constitution and the courts, statutes and the statute makers, soldier and dreadnaught, drayman and street sweep, cook, counselor, and clerk.

" I am the battle of yesterday, and the mistake of to-morrow.

" I am the mystery of the men who do without knowing why.

" I am the clutch of an idea, and the reasoned purpose of resolution.

" I am no more than what you believe me to be and I am all that you believe I can be.

" I am what you make me, nothing more.

" I swing before your eyes as a bright gleam of color, a symbol of yourself, the pictured suggestion of that big thing which makes this Nation. My stars and my stripes are your dream and your labors. They are bright with cheer, firm with faith, because you have made them so out of your hearts. For you are the makers of the flag and it is well that you glory in the making."

Ode to the Flag

Charles C. Crellin

STARS of the early dawning, set in a field of blue;
Stripes of the sunrise splendor, crimson and white of hue;
Flag o' our fathers' fathers born on the field of strife,
Phoenix of fiery battle risen from human life;
Given for God and freedom, sacred, indeed, the trust
Left by the countless thousands returned to the silent
    dust.

Flag of a mighty nation waving aloft unfurled;
Kissed by the sun of heaven, caressed by the winds of
    the world;
Greater than kingly power, greater than all mankind;
Conceived in the need of the hour, inspired by the Master
    Mind;
Over the living children, over the laureled grave,
Streaming on high in the cloudless sky, banner our fath-
    ers gave.

Flag of a new-born era, of every right
Wrung from a tyrant power, unawed by a tyrant's might;
Facing again the menace outflung from a foreign shore,
Meeting again the challenge as met in the years before;
Under thy spangled folds thy children await to give
All that they have or are that the flag they love shall
    live.

A Song for the Flag

Denis A. McCarthy

HERE is my love to you, flag of the free, and flag of the
    tried and true;
Here is my love to your streaming stripes and your stars
    in a field of blue;
Here is my love to your silken folds wherever they wave
    on high,
For you are the flag of a land for which 'twere sweet for
    a man to die.

Native or foreign, we're all as one when cometh the day
    of strife.
What is the dearest gift we can give for the flag but a
    human life?
Native or foreign are all the same when the heart's blood
    reddens the earth,
And, native or foreign, 'tis love like this is the ultimate
    test of your worth.

Native or immigrant, here is the task to which we must
    summon our powers:
Ever unsullied to keep the flag in peace as in war's wild
    hours.
Selfishness, narrowness, graft, and greed and the evil
    that hates the light —
All these are foes of the flag to-day; all these we must
    face and fight.

Symbol of hope to me and to mine and to all who aspire
    to be free,

Ever your golden stars may shine from the east to the
　　western sea;
Ever your golden stars may shine, and ever your stripes
　　may gleam,
To lead us from the deeds we do to the greater deeds
　　that we dream.

Here is our love to you, flag of the free, and flag of the
　　tried and true;
Here is our love to your streaming stripes and your stars
　　in a field of blue;
Native or foreign, we're children all of the land over
　　which you fly,
And, native or foreign, we love the land for which it
　　were sweet to die.

A Song for Flag Day

Lydia Avery Coonley Ward

OUT on the breeze,
　　O'er land and seas,
A beautiful banner is streaming.
　　Shining its stars,
　　Splendid its bars,
Under the sunshine 'tis gleaming.

Over the brave
　　Long may it wave,
Peace to the world ever bringing.
　　While to the stars,
　　Linked with the bars,
Hearts will forever be singing.

The American Boy

Anonymous

Son

" FATHER, look up and see that flag;
　How gracefully it flies!
Those pretty stripes — they seem to be
　A rainbow in the skies."

FATHER

" It is your country's flag, my son,
　And proudly drinks the light —
O'er ocean's waves, in foreign climes,
　A symbol of our might."

Son

" Father, what fearful noise is that,
　Like thundering of the clouds?
Why do the people wave their hats,
　And rush along in crowds?"

FATHER

" It is the loud-mouthed cannon's roar,
　The glad shouts of the Free;
This is the day to memory dear —
　'T is Freedom's Jubilee."

Son

" I wish that I were now a man;
　I'd fire my cannon, too,
And cheer as loudly as the rest —
　But, father, why don't you?"

FATHER

" I'm getting old and weak — but still
    My heart is big with joy;
I've witnessed many a day like this,—
    Shout you aloud, my boy."

SON

" Hurrah for Freedom's Jubliee!
    God bless our native land!
And may I live to hold the sword
    Of Freedom in my hand!"

FATHER

" Well done, my boy — forever love
    The land that gave you birth;
A home where Freedom loves to dwell —
    The happiest land on earth!"

The Little Flags

John Clair Minot

OH, when you see them flying
    Beside the summer way —
The little flags they put in place
    Upon Memorial Day —
Remember each is crying
    A message straight to you —
A message straight to every lad
    Whose heart is clean and true.

They tell the splendid story
    Of those who marched away

In answer to a voice that said,
  "Your country calls! Obey!"
They heard the call to glory,
  As you can, if you try:
"Your flag demands your best to-day,
Not some time, by and by!"

The Service Flag

William Herschell

DEAR little flag in the window there,
Hung with a tear and a woman's prayer;
Child of Old Glory, born with a star —
Oh, what a wonderful flag you are!

Blue is your star in its field of white,
Dipped in the red that was born of fight;
Born of the blood that our forbearers shed
To raise your mother, the Flag, o'erhead.

And now you've come in this frenzied day,
To speak from a window — to speak and say:
"I am the voice of a soldier-son
Gone to be gone till the victory's won.

"I am the flag of the service, sir;
The flag of his mother — I speak for her
Who stands by my window and waits and fears,
But hides from the others her unwept tears.

"I am the flag of the wives who wait
For the safe return of a martial mate,
A mate gone forth where the war god thrives
To save from sacrifice others men's wives.

" I am the flag of the sweethearts true;
The often unthought of — the sisters, too.
I am the flag of a mother's son
And won't come down till the victory's won!"

Dear little flag in the window there,
Hung with a tear and a woman's prayer;
Child of Old Glory, born with a star —
Oh, what a wonderful flag you are!

Betsy's Battle Flag

Minna Irving

FROM dusk till dawn the livelong night
She kept the tallow dips alight,
And fast her nimble fingers flew
To sew the stars upon the blue.
With weary eyes and aching head
She stitched the stripes of white and red,
And when the day came up the stair
Complete across a carven chair
　　Hung Betsy's battle flag.

Like shadows in the evening gray
The Continentals filed away,
With broken boots and ragged coats,
But hoarse defiance in their throats;
They bore the marks of want and cold,
And some were lame and some were old,
And some with wounds untended bled,
But floating bravely overhead
　　Was Betsy's battle flag.

When fell the battle's leaden rain,
The soldier hushed his moans of pain
And raised his dying head to see
King George's troopers turn and flee.
Their charging column reeled and broke,
And vanished in the rolling smoke,
Before the glory of the stars,
The snowy stripes, and scarlet bars
   Of Betsy's battle flag.

The simple stone of Betsy Ross
Is covered now with mold and moss,
But still her deathless banner flies,
And keeps the color of the skies.
A nation thrills, a nation bleeds,
A nation follows where it leads,
And every man is proud to yield
His life upon a crimson field
   For Betsy's battle flag!

The Conquered Banner

Abram J. Ryan

FURL that banner, for 'tis weary;
Round its staff 'tis drooping dreary;
   Furl it, fold it, it is best;
For there's not a man to wave it,
And there's not a sword to save it,
And there's not one left to lave it
In the blood which heroes gave it;
And its foes now scorn and brave it;
   Furl it, hide it; let it rest!

Take that banner down! 'tis tattered;
Broken is its staff and shattered;
And the valiant hosts are scattered
   Over whom it floated high.
Oh! 'tis hard for us to fold it;
Hard to think there's none to hold it;
Hard that those who once unrolled it
   Now must furl it with a sigh.

Furl that banner! furl it sadly!
Once ten thousands hailed it gladly,
And ten thousands wildly, madly,
   Swore it should forever wave;
Swore that foeman's sword should never
Hearts like theirs entwined dissever
And that flag should float forever
   O'er their freedom or their grave.

Furl it! for the hands that grasped it,
And the hearts that fondly clasped it,
   Cold and dead are lying low;
And that banner — it is trailing,
While around it sounds the wailing
   Of its people in their woe.

For, though conquered, they adore it,
Love the cold, dead hands that bore it,
Weep for those who fell before it,
Pardon those who trailed and tore it,—
But, oh, wildly they deplore it,
   Now to furl and fold it so!

Furl that banner! True, 'tis gory,
Yet 'tis wreathed around with glory,

And 'twill live in song and story,
  Though its folds are in the dust;
For its fame on brightest pages,
Penned by poets and by sages,
Shall go sounding down the ages —
  Furl its folds though now we must.

Furl that banner, softly, slowly!
Treat it gently — it is holy —
  For it droops above the dead.
Touch it not — unfold it never,
Let it droop there, furled forever,
  For its people's hopes are fled.

When Old Glory Came to Stay

Walter S. Gard

" For America is not the magic scenery
Washed by the sunrise and the sunset seas;
No; nor yet the prairies dark with herds,
Or land-lakes of the western grain; nor yet,
Wonder cities white-towered, nor the peaks
Bursting with metals, nor the smoky mills,
America is you and you and I."

IT was in April just 102 years ago that the flag you
know as " Old Glory" came to stay. It had its birthday
on June 14, 1777, but it was in the first green month of
spring, 1818, that the starry banner became finally fixed
in the skies of the nations. One year after the Declaration of Independence, Congress by resolution created a
flag with alternating red and white stripes and a blue field

carrying thirteen white stars. Forty-one years later the law was enacted which decreed its permanent form.

Did you know that until April 4, 1818, the date we celebrate this month, the American flag could as properly have been made with perpendicular stripes as with the familiar horizontal ones? That every flag-maker at that time was following his own whim concerning the number of stripes the flag should contain? Did you know that although it had a sort of general form based upon habit, the American flag was being shifted about, a shapeless, wandering sort of national emblem, which seemed certain to grow so unwieldy and awkward that its use as a flag was threatened?

Peter H. Wendover, a representative of New York state, wishing to put an end to the uncertainty about the flag, introduced in Congress the act " To establish the flag of the United States." It directed that the flag be thirteen horizontal stripes, alternate red and white, and in the blue field a white star for each state in the Union. The new star must be added not later than the fourth day of July following admission of the state. The act was passed by Congress on March 31, 1818, and four days later President Monroe signed it. His pen gave the fourth day of April an importance which has long been overlooked, but Juniors who love the flag will carry that date in their memories.

Many stories exist concerning the planning and making of the first Stars and Stripes, but all agree that the honor of giving the rippling banner its most familiar name belongs to William Driver, a Salem, Massachusetts, sailor. In 1831 Captain Driver was presented with an American flag to fly from the masthead of his brig. Immediately he christened it " Old Glory."

" Your Flag, and my Flag!
　　And oh, how much it holds —
Your land and my land —
　　Secure within its folds!
Your heart and my heart
　　Beat quicker at the sight;
Sun-kissed and wind-tossed,
　　Red and blue and white,
The one Flag — the great Flag — the Flag for me and
　　you —
Glorified all else beside — the red and white and blue."

The American's Creed

William Tyler Page

Reprinted from the authorized version

I BELIEVE in the United States of America as a Government of the people, by the people, for the people; whose just powers are derived from the consent of the governed; a democracy in a Republic; a sovereign Nation of many sovereign States; a perfect Union, one and inseparable; established upon those principles of freedom, equality, justice and humanity for which American patriots sacrificed their lives and fortunes.

I therefore believe it is my duty to my country to love it; to support its Constitution; to obey its laws; to respect its flag; and to defend it against all enemies.

Quotations for Flag Day

The first real American flag has its origin in the following resolution adopted by the American Congress, June 14, 1777: " Resolved, That the flag of the thirteen United States be thirteen stripes alternate red and white; that the union be thirteen stars; white in a blue field, representing a new constellation."

Fling it from mast and steeple,
  Symbol o'er land and sea
Of the life of a happy people,
  Gallant and strong and free.
Proudly we view its colors,
  Flag of the brave and true,
With the clustered stars and the steadfast bars,
  The red, the white, and the blue.
                                    — *Margaret E. Sangster.*

She's up there,— Old Glory,— how bright the stars stream!
And the stripes like red signals of liberty gleam!
And we dare for her, living, or dream the last dream,
'Neath the flag of our country forever!
                                    — *Frank L. Stanton.*

One flag, one land, one heart, one hand,
  One nation, evermore.
                                    — *Oliver Wendell Holmes.*

Our flag carries American ideas, American history, and American feelings. Beginning with the colonies, and coming down to our time, in its sacred heraldry, in its glorious insignia, it has gathered and stored chiefly this supreme idea — *divine right of liberty in man.* Every color means liberty; every thread means liberty; every form of star and beam or stripe of light means liberty; not lawlessness, not license; but organized institutional liberty,— liberty through law, and law for liberty.— *Henry Ward Beecher.*

Behold it! Listen to it! Every star has a tongue; every stripe is articulate. "There is no language or speech where their voices are not heard." There is magic in the web of it. It has an answer for every question of duty. It has a solution for every doubt and perplexity. It has a word of cheer for every hour of gloom or of despondency. Behold it! Listen to it! It speaks of earlier and of later struggles. It speaks of victories, and sometimes of reverses, on the sea and on the land. It speaks of patriots and heroes among the living and the dead. But before all and above all other associations and memories, whether of glorious men, or glorious deeds, or glorious places, its voice is ever of Union and Liberty, of the Constitution and the Laws.— *Robert C. Winthrop.*

All hail to our glorious ensign! Courage to the heart, and strength to the hand to which, in all time, it shall be entrusted! May it ever wave in honor, in unsullied glory, and patriotic hope, on the dome of the capitol, on the dome of the country's stronghold, on the tented plain, on the wave-rocked top mast. Wherever, on the earth's surface, the eye of the American shall behold it, may he have reason to bless it! On whatever spot it is planted, humanity a brave champion, and religion an altar. Though stained with blood in a righteous cause, may it never, in any cause be stained with shame. Alike, when its gorgeous folds shall wanton in lazy holiday triumphs on the summer breeze, and its tattered fragments be dimly seen through the clouds of war, may it be the pride and the joy of the American heart. First raised in the cause of right and liberty, in that cause alone may it forever spread its streaming blazonry to the battle and the storm. Having been borne victoriously across the continent, and on every sea, may virtue, and freedom, and peace forever follow where it leads the way.— *Edward Everett.*

There is the national flag! It must be cold, indeed, who can look upon its folds, rippling in the breeze, without pride of country. If he be in a foreign land, the flag is companionship, and country itself, with all its endearments. Its highest beauty is in what it symbolizes. It is because it represents all, that all gaze at it with delight and reverence. It is a piece of bunting lifted in the air; but it speaks sublimely, and every part has a voice. Its stripes, of alternate red and white, proclaim the original union of thirteen States to maintain the Declaration of Independence. Its stars, white on a field of blue, proclaim that union of States, constituting our national constellation, which receives a new star with every new State. The two, together, signify union, past and present. The very colors have a language, which was officially recognized by our fathers. White is for purity, red for valor, blue for justice, and all together,— bunting, stars, stripes, and colors blazing in the sky — make the flag of our country, to be cherished by all of our hearts, to be upheld by all our hands.— *Charles Sumner.*

Let us make up our mind that when we do put a new star upon our banner it shall be a fixed one, never to be dimmed by the horrors of war, but brightened by the contentment and prosperity of peace. Let us go on to extend the area of our usefulness, add star upon star, until our light shall shine upon millions of a free and happy people.— *Abraham Lincoln.*

O God of our fathers! this banner must shine
Where battle is hottest, in warfare divine!
The cannon has thundered, the bugle has blown,
We fear not the summons, we fight not alone!
O lead us, till wide from the gulf to the sea
The land shall be sacred to freedom and Thee!
With love for oppression, with blessing for scars
One Country, one Banner, the Stripes and the Stars.
— *Edna Dean Proctor.*

When Freedom, from her mountain height,
Unfurled her standard to the air,

She tore the azure robe of Night,
  And set the stars of glory there.
She mingled with its gorgeous dyes
  The milky baldric of the skies,
And striped its pure, celestial white,
  With streakings of the morning light:
Then, from his mansion in the sun,
  She called her eagle bearer down,
And gave into his mighty hand
  The symbol of her chosen land.

. . . . . , . . ӡ

Flag of the free hearts' hope and home!
  By angel hands to valor given!
Thy stars have lit the welkin dome,
  And all thy hues were born in Heaven.
Forever float that standard sheet!
  Where breathes the foe but falls before us,
With Freedom's soil beneath our feet,
  And Freedom's banner streaming o'er us?
                    — *J. Rodman Drake.*

This nation has a banner, too; and wherever it has streamed abroad, men have seen day break bursting on their eyes, for the American flag has been the symbol of liberty, and men have rejoiced in it. Not another flag on the globe has such an errand, or went forth upon the sea, carrying everywhere, the world around, such hope for the captive and such glorious tidings. The stars upon it were to the pining nations like the morning stars of God and the stripes upon it were beams of morning light.

In all the world is there another banner that carries such hope, such grandeur of spirit, such soul-inspiring truth, as our dear old American flag? Made by liberty, made for liberty, nourished in its spirit, carried in its service, and never, not once, in all the earth made to stoop to despotism!
— *Henry Ward Beecher.*

Let us twine each thread of the glorious tissues of our country's flag about our heart strings; and, looking upon our homes and catching the spirit that breathes upon us from the battle fields of our fathers, let us resolve, come weal or woe, we will, in life and in death, now and forever, stand by the Stars and Stripes.— *Henry Ward Beecher*.

O bright flag, O brave flag, O flag to lead the free,
The hand of God thy colors blent,
And heaven to earth thy glory lent,
To shield the weak, and guide the strong,
To make an end of human wrong,
And draw a countless human host to follow after thee!
— *Henry Van Dyke*.

By the driven snow-white and the living blood-red
Of my bars and their heaven of stars overhead —
By the symbol conjoined of them all, skyward cast,
As I float from the steeple or flags at the mast,
Or droop o'er the sod where the long grasses nod,—
My name is as old as the glory of God,
So I came by the name of " Old Glory."
— *James Whitcomb Riley*.

Our flag carries American ideas, American history, American feelings.— *Henry Ward Beecher*.

So long as that flag shall bear aloft its glittering stars — bearing them amidst the din of battle, and waving them triumphantly above the storms of the ocean, so long, I trust, shall the rights of American citizens be preserved safe and unimpaired.— *Samuel Houston*.

Your flag and my flag!
  And, oh, how much it holds —
Your land and my land —
  Secure within its folds!
Your heart and my heart
  Beat quicker at the sight;

Sun-kissed and wind-tossed —
Red and blue and white.
The one flag — the great flag — the flag for me and you —
Glorified all else beside — the red and white and blue!
— *Wilbur D. Nesbit.*

Ours is the only flag that has in reality written upon it
" Liberty, Equality, Fraternity "— the three grandest words
in all the languages of men.— *Robert G. Ingersoll.*

O folds of white and scarlet! O blue field with your
stars! May fond eyes welcome you, and dying lips give you
their blessing! Ours by inheritance, ours by allegiance,
ours by affection, long may you float on the free winds of
heaven, the emblem of liberty, the hope of the world.—
Anonymous.

Guard well that flag, for faith and hope and better days to be,
Your flag, my flag, the people's flag,
The flag that makes men free!
— *Kate Brownlee Sherwood.*

Wave, priceless banner of the free,
In majesty, from sea to sea!
With buoyant heart from gulf to lake
Shall freedom follow in thy wake —
Old Glory.
— *J. H. Mackley.*

Boldly we wave its colors,
Our veins are thrilled anew,
By the steadfast bars, the clustered stars,
The red, the white and the blue.
— *Margaret E. Sangster.*

Its stripes of red, eternal dyed with heart-streams of all
lands;
Its white, the snow-capped hills that hide in storm their
upraised hands;

Its blue, the ocean waves that beat 'round freedom's circled
    shore.

—James Whitcomb Riley.

Do not be ashamed to love the flag or to confess your love
for it.

Make much of it; tell its history; sing of it.

It now floats over our schools and it ought to hang from
the windows of all our homes on all public days.

— Benjamin Harrison.

Our flag has never been trailed in the dust of dishonor
and to-day it proudly floats from the masthead of vessels in
all waters and is honored and respected by every country on
the globe.— *Mary M. North.*

The Star-Spangled Banner! Was ever flag so beautiful,
did ever flag so fill the souls of men? The love of woman;
the sense of duty; the thirst for glory; the heart-throbbing
that impels the humblest American to stand by his colors
fearless in the defense of his native soil and holding it
sweet to die for it — the yearning which draws him to it
when exiled from it — its free institutions and its blessed
memories, all are embodied and symbolized by the broad
stripes and bright stars of the nation's emblem.— *Henry
Watterson.*

The Republic never retreats. Its flag is the *only* flag that
has never known defeat. Where that flag leads we follow,
for we know that the hand that bears it onward is the
unseen hand of God. We follow the flag and independence
is ours. We follow the flag and nationality is ours. Everywhere and always it means larger liberty, nobler opportunity,
and greater human happiness.— *Albert J. Beveridge.*

It expresses the will of a free people, and proclaims that
they are supreme and that they acknowledge no earthly sovereign but themselves. Glorious old banner.— *William Mc-
Kinley.*

And wherever that flag has gone it has been a herald of a better day — it has been the pledge of freedom, of justice, of order, of civilization, and of Christianity. Tyrants only hate it. All who sigh for the triumph of righteousness and truth salute and love it.— *A. P. Putnam.*

The flag stands for all that we hold dear — freedom, democracy, government of the people, by the people, for the people. These are the great principles for which the flag stands, and when that democracy and that freedom and that government of the people are in danger, then it is our duty to defend the flag which stands for them all, and in order to defend the flag and keep it soaring as it soars here to-day, undimmed, unsullied, victorious over the years, we must be ready to defend it, and like the men of '76 and '61 pledge to it our lives, our fortunes, and our sacred honor.— *Henry Cabot Lodge.*

> For your name,— just to hear it,
> Repeat it, and cheer it, 's a tang to the spirit
> As salt as a tear: —
> And seeing you fly, and the boys marching by,
> There's a shout in the throat and a blur in the eye,
> And an aching to live for you always — or die,
> If dying, we still keep you waving on high.
>   — *James Whitcomb Riley.*

> Right nobly do you lead the way, Old Flag.
> Your stars shine out for liberty,
> Your white stripes stand for purity,
> Your crimson claims that courage high
> For Honor's sake to fight and die.
> Lead on against the alien shore!
> We'll follow you e'en to Death's door, Old Flag.
>   — *Hubbard Parker.*

The flag of America stands for the Rights of man, to shelter the oppressed and to guarantee to every citizen Life, Liberty, and the Pursuit of Happiness.

Other flags may have a glorious past, but the Stars and Stripes stands for a glorious future. It is the bud of promise for generations of men, fighting for freedom, for a living wage, and for opportunity to advance the cause of humanity. When the band plays the " Star Spangled Banner " stand with uncovered head, in reverence for the principles for which the Flag stands, and in the presence of the Flag, take off your hat, for our hopes of righting the wrongs of man, are symbolized by our feelings as we honor our National emblem.— *Elroy Headley.*

Thank God we can see in the glory of morn,
The invincible flag that our fathers defended,
And our hearts can repeat what the heroes have sworn
That war shall not end till the war-lust is ended.
Then the blood-thirsty sword shall no longer be lord
Of the nations oppressed by the conqueror's horde,
And the banners of freedom shall peacefully wave,
O'er the world of the free and the lands of the brave.
— *Henry Van Dyke.*

Under the " starry flag," there are equal rights for all.— *Andrew Carnegie.*

We follow, all of us, one flag. It symbolizes our purposes and our aspirations; it represents what we believe and what we mean to maintain, and wherever it floats, it is the flag of the free and the hope of the oppressed, and wherever and whenever it is assailed, at any sacrifice it will be carried to a triumphant peace.— *William McKinley.*

May our lives to-day be bound anew in loyalty to our beloved land. May we ever be true in our patriotism, loyal in our love, and may the God of nations so rule in the hearts of men that when we shall come to pass over to the silent majority, the rest behind the sunset hills, our eyes may, as we pass, salute the flag, unstained and unconquered. — *Thomas E. Green.*

I come with a full heart and a steady hand to salute the flag that floats above me; my flag and your flag; the flag of the Union; the flag of the free heart's hope and home; the star spangled banner of our fathers; the flag that, uplifted triumphantly over a few brave men, has never been obscured; destined by God to waft on its ample folds the eternal song of manhood — freedom to all the world — the emblem of the power on earth which is to exceed that on which it was said the sun never went down.— *Henry W. Watterson.*

It is the flag that guards our citadels of justice and national honor.

It is the ensign of the government of the people, by the people, and for the people.

It is the pillar of cloud by day and the pillar of fire by night to guide our children and our children's children and their descendants along the pathway of intelligence, virtue, integrity and honor forevermore.

And as we near the shores of the Eternal Morning, the old flag lifts the soul to new visions of the future glory of our common country.— *Selected.*

We join ourselves to no party that does not carry the flag and keep step to the music of the union.— *Rufus Choate.*

> Behold, its streaming rays unite,
> One mingling flood of braided light;
> The red that fires the southern rose,
> With spotless white from northern snows,
> And, spangled o'er its azure, see,
> The sister stars of liberty.
> > Then hail the Banner of the Free,
> > The starry flower of Liberty!
> > > — *Oliver Wendell Holmes.*

I love the name of Washington,
  I love my country, too;
I love the flag, the dear old flag,
  Of red and white and blue.
                              — Selected.

Then, up with our flag! — let it stream on the air,
  Though our fathers are cold in their graves,
They had hands that could strike, they had souls that could
    dare,
  And their sons were not born to be slaves.
Up, up with that banner; where'er it may call,
  Our millions shall rally around,
And a nation of freemen that moment shall fall
  When its stars shall be trailed on the ground.
                              — George Washington Cutter.

A song for our banner? The watchword recall
  Which gave the republic her station;
"United we stand, divided we fall!"
  It made and preserved us a nation!
                              — Geo. P. Morris.

O'er the high and o'er the lowly
Floats that banner bright and holy,
  In the rays of freedom's sun;
In the nation's heart embedded,
O'er our Union newly wedded,
  One in all, and all in one.

As it floated long before us,
Be it ever floating o'er us,
  O'er our land from shore to shore;
There are freemen yet to wave it,
Millions who would die to save it,
  Wave it, save it evermore.
                              — Dexter Smith.

O folds of white and scarlet! O blue field with your silver stars! May fond eyes welcome you, willing feet follow you, strong hands defend you, warm hearts cherish you, and dying lips give you their blessing! Ours by inheritance, ours by allegiance, ours by affection,— long may you float on the free winds of heaven, the emblem of liberty, the hope of the world! — *Selected*.

> Flag of the free, heart's hope and home,
> By angel hands to valor given,
> Thy stars have lit the welkin dome,
> And all thy hues were born in heaven.
> — *Drake*.

Having learned to stand by the flag, we must also learn to stand by what the flag symbolizes; to stand up for equal rights, universal freedom, for justice to all, for a true democracy.— *James Freeman Clarke*.

No matter what happens to you, no matter who flatters you never look at another flag, never let a night pass that you do not pray to God to bless that flag. Remember, that behind all these men you have to deal with, behind officers, and government, and people even, there is the Country Herself, your Country, and that you belong to your own mother. Stand by her as you would stand by your own mother.— *Edward Everett Hale*.

All who stand beneath our banner are free. Ours is the only flag that has in reality written upon it Liberty, Fraternity, Equality, the three grandest words in all the language of men.— *Robert G. Ingersoll*.

In the war for independence America had but one object in view, for in independence are concentrated and condensed every blessing that makes life desirable, every right and privilege which can tend to the happiness, or secure the native dignity, of man.— *John Lathrop.*

INDEPENDENCE DAY

July 4

Independence Day celebrates the signing of the Declaration of Independence on July 4th, 1776, by the members of the Continental Congress, then assembled at the State House in Philadelphia. The event was first celebrated on July 8, 1776, when the Declaration of Independence was read to the crowds of people assembled outside the State House. That night there were bonfires, ringing of bells and other demonstrations of joy. Each recurring 4th of July was observed by the army, and, since the Revolutionary War, has been made a legal holiday in every State, Territory and possession of the United States.

American Independence

A. B. Street

HAIL to the planting of Liberty's tree!
Hail to the charter declaring us free!
Millions of voices are chanting its praises,
  Millions of worshippers bend at its shrine,
Wherever the sun of America blazes
  Wherever the stars of our bright banner shine.

Sing to the heroes who breasted the flood
That, swelling, rolled o'er them — a deluge of blood,
Fearless they clung to the ark of the nation,
  And dashed on mid lightning, and thunder, and blast,
Till Peace, like the dove, brought her breach of salvation,
  And Liberty's mount was their refuge at last.

Bright is the beautiful land of our birth,
The home of the homeless all over the earth.
Oh! let us ever with fondest devotion,
  The freedom our fathers bequeathed us, watch o'er
Till the angel shall stand on the earth and the ocean,
  And shout mid earth's ruins, that Time is no more.

Independence Bell

Anonymous

THERE was tumult in the city,
  In the quaint old Quaker town,
And the streets were rife with people,
  Pacing restless up and down;

People gathering at corners,
　　Where they whispered, each to each,
And the sweat stood on their temples,
　　With the earnestness of speech.

As the bleak Atlantic currents
　　Lash the wild Newfoundland shore,
So they beat against the State House,
　　So they surged against the door;
And the mingling of their voices
　　Made a harmony profound,
Till the quiet street of chestnuts
　　Was all turbulent with sound.

" Will they do it? "　" Dare they do it? "
　　" Who is speaking? "　" What's the news? "
" What of Adams? "　" What of Sherman? "
　　" Oh, God grant they won't refuse! "
" Make some way, there! "　" Let me nearer! "
　　" I am stifling! "—" Stifle, then:
When a nation's life's at hazard,
　　We've no time to think of men! "

So they beat against the portal —
　　Man and woman, maid and child;
And the July sun in heaven
　　On the scene looked down and smiled;
The same sun that saw the Spartan
　　Shed his patriot blood in vain,
Now beheld the soul of freedom,
　　All unconquered, rise again.

Aloft in that high steeple
　　Sat the bellman, old and gray;

He was weary of the tyrant
　　And his iron-sceptered sway;
So he sat with one hand ready
　　On the clapper of the bell,
Till his eye should catch the signal
　　Of the happy news to tell.

See! Oh, see! the dense crowd quivers
　　All along the lengthening line,
As the boy from out the portal
　　Rushes forth to give the sign!
With his little hands uplifted,
　　Breezes dallying with his hair,
Hark! with deep, clear intonation,
　　Breaks his young voice on the air.

Hushed the people's swelling murmur,
　　List the boy's exultant cry.
"Ring!" he souths aloud; "ring! Grandpa!
　　Ring! Oh, ring for Liberty!"
Instantly, upon the signal,
　　The old bellman lifts his hand,
Forth he sends the good news, making
　　Iron music through the land.

How they shouted! What rejoicing!
　　How the old bell shook the air,
Till the clang of freedom ruffled
　　The calm, gliding Delaware!
How the bonfires and the torches
　　Lighted up the night's repose;
And from out the flames, like Phoenix,
　　Glorious Liberty arose!

That old State House bell is silent,
   Hushed is now its clamorous tongue,
But the spirit it awakened
   Still is living — ever young.
And whene'er we greet the sunlight
   On the Fourth of each July,
We will ne'er forget the bellman
   Who, betwixt the earth and sky,
Rung out our independence,
   Which, please God, shall never die!

Freedom, Our Queen

Oliver Wendell Holmes

LAND where the banners wave last in the sun,
   Blazoned with star-clusters, many in one,
Floating o'er prairie and mountain and sea;
   Hark! 'tis the voice of thy children to thee!

Here at thine altar our vows we renew
   Still in thy cause to be loyal and true,—
True to thy flag on the field and the wave,
   Living to honor it, dying to save!

Mother of heroes! if perfidy's blight
   Fall on a star in thy garland of light,
Sound but one bugle-blast! Lo! at the sign
   Armies all panoplied wheel into line.

Hope of the world; thou hast broken its chains —
   Wear they bright arms while a tyrant remains,
Stand for the right till the nations shall own
   Freedom their sovereign with Law for her throne!

Freedom! sweet Freedom! our voices resound,
  Queen by God's blessing, unsceptred, uncrowned!
Freedom, sweet Freedom, our pulses repeat,
  Warm with her life-blood, as long as they beat!

Fold the broad banner-stripes over her breast —
  Crown her with star-jewels Queen of the West!
Earth for her heritage, God for her friend,
  She shall reign over us world without end!

Paul Revere's Ride

Henry Wadsworth Longfellow

LISTEN, my children, and you shall hear
Of the midnight ride of Paul Revere,
On the eighteenth of April, in seventy-five:
Hardly a man is now alive
Who remembers that famous day and year.

He said to his friend, " If the British march
By land or sea from the town to-night,
Hang a lantern aloft in the belfry arch
Of the North Church tower as a signal-light,
One, if by land, and two, if by sea;
And I on the opposite shore will be,
Ready to ride and spread the alarm
Through every Middlesex village and farm,
For the country folk to be up and to arm."

Then he said, Good night! and with muffled oar
Silently rowed to the Charlestown shore,
Just as the moon rose over the bay,
Where swinging wide at her moorings lay

The *Somerset,* British man-of-war;
A phantom ship, with each mast and spar
Across the moon like a prison bar,
And a huge black hulk, that was magnified
By its own reflection in the tide.

Meanwhile, his friend, through alley and street
Wanders and watches with eager ears,
Till in the silence around him he hears
The muster of men at the barrack door,
The sound of arms, and the tramp of feet,
And the measured tread of the grenadiers,
Marching down to their boats on the shore.

Then he climbed to the tower of the Old North Church,
By the wooden stairs, with stealthy tread,
To the belfry-chamber overhead,
And startled the pigeons from their perch
On the sombre rafters, that round him made
Masses of moving shapes of shade —,
By the trembling ladder, steep and tall,
To the highest window in the wall,
Where he paused to listen and look down
A moment on the roofs of the town,
And the moolight flowing over all.

Beneath, in the churchyard, lay the dead,
In their night-encampment on the hill,
Wrapped in silence so deep and still
That he could hear, like a sentinel's tread,
The watchful night-wind, as it went
Creeping along from tent to tent,
And seeming to whisper, " All is well! "
A moment only he feels the spell

Of the place and the hour, and the secret dread
Of the lonely belfry and the dead;
For suddenly all his thoughts are bent
On a shadowy something far away,
Where the river widens to meet the bay,—
A line of black that bends and floats
On the rising tide, like a bridge of boats.

Meanwhile, impatient to mount and ride,
Booted and spurred, with a heavy stride
On the opposite shore walked Paul Revere.
Now he patted his horse's side,
Now gazed at the landscape far and near,
Then, impetuous, stamped the earth,
And turned and tightened his saddle-girth;
But mostly be watched with eager search
The belfry-tower of the Old North Church,
As it rose above the graves on the hill,
Lonely, and spectral, and sombre and still.
And lo! as he looks, on the belfry's height
A glimmer, and then a gleam of light!
He springs to the saddle, the bridle he turns,
But lingers and gazes, till full on his sight,
A second lamp in the belfry burns!

A hurry of hoofs in a village street,
A shape in the moonlight, a bulk in the dark,
And beneath, from the pebbles, in passing, a spark
Struck out by a steed flying fearless and fleet;
That was all! And yet, through the gloom and the light.
The fate of a nation was riding that night;
And the spark struck out by that steed, in his flight,
Kindled the land into flame with its heat.

He has left the village and mounted the steep,
And beneath him, tranquil and broad and deep,
Is the Mystic, meeting the ocean tides;
And under the alders, that skirt its edge,
Now soft on the sand, now loud on the ledge,
Is heard the tramp of his steed as he rides.
It was twelve by the village clock
When he crossed the bridge into Medford town.
He heard the crowing of the cock,
And the barking of the farmer's dog,
And felt the damp of the river fog,
That rises after the sun goes down.

It was one by the village clock,
When he rode into Lexington.
He saw the gilded weathercock
Swim in the moonlight as he passed,
And the meeting-house windows, blank and bare,
Gaze at him with a spectral glare,
As if they already stood aghast
At the bloody work they would look upon.

It was two by the village clock,
When he came to the bridge in Concord town.
He heard the bleating of the flock,
And the twitter of birds among the trees,
And felt the breath of the morning breeze
Blowing over the meadows brown.
And one was safe and asleep in his bed
Who at the bridge would be first to fall,
Who that day would be lying dead,
Pierced by a British musket-ball.

You know the rest. In the books you have read,
How the British Regulars fired and fled —
How the farmers gave them ball for ball,
From behind each fence and farm-yard wall,
Chasing the red-coats down the lane,
Then crossing the fields to emerge again
Under the trees at the turn of the road,
And only pausing to fire and load.

So through the night rode Paul Revere;
And so through the night went his cry of alarm
To every Middlesex village and farm —
A cry of defiance and not of fear,
A voice in the darkness, a knock at the door,
And a word that shall echo forevermore!
For, borne on the night-wind of the Past,
Through all our history, to the last,
In the hour of darkness and peril and need,
The people will waken and listen to hear,
The hurrying hoof-beats of that steed,
And the midnight message of Paul Revere.

On the Eve of Bunker Hill

Clinton Scollard

'Twas June on the face of the earth, June with the rose's
　　breath,
When life is a gladsome thing, and a distant dream is
　　death;
There was gossip of birds in the air, and the lowing of
　　herds by the wood,
And a sunset gleam in the sky that the heart of a man
　　holds good;

Then the nun-like Twilight came, violet-vestured and
    still,
And the night's first star outshone afar on the eve of
    Bunker Hill.

There rang a cry through the camp, with its word upon
    rousing word;
There was never a faltering foot in the ranks of those
    that heard; —
Lads from the Hampshire hills and the rich Connecticut
    vales,
Sons of the old Bay Colony, from its shores and its
    inland dales;
Swiftly they fell in line; no fear could their valor chill;
Ah, brave the show as they ranged a-row on the eve of
    Bunker Hill!

Then a deep voice lifted a prayer to the God of the brave
    and the true,
And the heads of the men were bare in the gathering
    dusk and dew;
The heads of a thousand men were bowed as the plead-
    ing rose,—
Smite Thou, Lord, as of old Thou smotest Thy people's
    foes!
Oh, nerve Thy servants' arms to work with a mighty
    will!
A hush, and then a loud Amen! on the eve of Bunker
    Hill!

Now they are gone through the night with never a thought
    of fame,
Gone to the field of a fight that shall win them a death-
    less name;

Some shall never again behold the set of the sun,
But lie like the Concord slain, and the slain of Lexington,
Martyrs to Freedom's cause.   Ah, how at their deeds we
   thrill,
The men whose might made strong the height on the eve
   of Bunker Hill!

The Sword of Bunker Hill

William Rose Wallace

HE lay upon his dying bed:
   His eye was growing dim,
When with a feeble voice he called
   His weeping son to him:
" Weep not, my boy! " the veteran said,
   " I bow to Heaven's high will —
But quickly from yon antlers bring
   The sword of Bunker Hill."

The sword was brought, the soldier's eye
   Lit with a sudden flame;
And as he grasped the ancient blade,
   He murmured Warren's name;
Then said, " My boy, I leave you gold —
   But what is richer still,
I leave you, mark me, mark me now —
   The sword of Bunker Hill.

" 'Twas on that dread, immortal day,
   I dared the Briton's band,
A captain raised this blade on me —
   I tore it from his hand;

And while the glorious battle raged,
  It lightened freedom's will —
For, boy, the God of freedom blessed
  The sword of Bunker Hill.

" Oh, keep the sword! "— his accents broke —
  A smile — and he was dead —
But his wrinkled hand still grasped the blade
  Upon that dying bed.
The son remains; the sword remains —
  Its glory growing still —
And twenty millions bless the sire,
  And sword of Bunker Hill.

Warren's Address

John Pierpont

STAND! the ground's your own, my braves!
Will ye give it up to slaves?
Will ye look for greener graves?
  Hope ye mercy still?
What's the mercy despots feel?
Hear it in that battle peal!
Read it on yon bristling steel!
  Ask it — ye who will.

Fear ye foes who kill for hire?
Will ye to your homes retire?
Look behind you! — they're afire!
  And, before you, see
Who have done it! From the vale
On they come! — And will ye quail?
Leaden rain and iron hail
  Let their welcome be!

In the God of battles trust!
Die we may — and die we must;
But, oh, where can dust to dust
  Be consigned so well,
As where heaven its dews shall shed
On the martyred patriot's bed,
And the rocks shall raise their head,
  Of his deeds to tell?

Concord Hymn

Ralph Waldo Emerson

By the rude bridge that arched the flood,
  Their flag to April's breeze unfurled,
Here once the embattled farmers stood,
  And fired the shot heard round the world.

The foe long since in silence slept;
  Alike the conqueror silent sleeps;
And Time, the ruined bridge has swept
  Down the dark stream which seaward creeps.

On the green bank, by this soft stream,
  We set to-day a votive stone;
That memory may their deed redeem,
  When like our sires, our sons are gone.

Spirit that made these heroes dare
  To die and leave their children free,
Bid Time and Nature gently spare
  The shaft we raise to them and thee.

New England's Dead

Isaac McLellan, Jr.

NEW ENGLAND'S Dead!   New England's dead!
  On every hill they lie;
On every field of strife made red
  By bloody victory.
Each valley, where the battle poured
  Its red and awful tide,
Beheld the brave New England sword
  With slaughter deeply dyed.
Their bones are on the northern hill,
  And on the southern plain,
By brook and river, lake and rill
  And by the roaring main.

The land is holy where they fought,
  And holy where they fell;
For by their blood that land was bought,
  The land they loved so well.
Then glory to that valiant band,
  The honored saviours of the land!
Oh! few and weak their numbers were —
  A handful of brave men;
But to their God they gave their prayer,
  And rushed to battle then.
And God of battles heard their cry,
  And sent to them the victory.

They left the ploughshare in the mould,
  Their flocks and herds without a fold,
The sickle in the unshorn grain,
  The corn, half garnered, on the plain;

And mustered in their simple dress,
    For wrongs to seek a stern redress;
To right those wrongs, come weal, come woe;
    To perish or o'ercome their foe.

And where are ye, O fearless men?
    And where are ye to-day?
I call: the hills reply again
    That ye have passed away;
That on old Bunker's lonely height,
    In Trenton and in Monmouth ground,
The grass grows green, the harvest bright,
    Above each soldier's mound.
The bugle's wild and warlike blast
    Shall muster them no more;
An army now might thunder past,
    And they not heed its roar.
The starry flag, 'neath which they fought
    In many a bloody day,
From their old graves shall rouse them not,
    For they have passed away.

Independence Day To-day

Margaret E. Sangster

OVER the mists of a century they come, and their tramp-
    ing feet
Are light as the dust on the broad highway, or the wind
    that sways in the wheat;
Out of the haze of the years between their shadowy hands
    stretch wide
To welcome the heroes home again who have fought for
    their cause and died.

They went to battle at Concord Bridge, and they fell on
    Bunker Hill;
The odds were great, but they struggled on with a stub-
    born Yankee will;
They lay in the fields at Lexington when the sun in the
    west was red,
And the next year's violets grew on the spot where their
    valiant blood was shed.

But they won in the end — with their broken guns and
    without much food to spare,
Won at the end of a bitter war, by means that they knew
    were fair;
And some of them wandered back to their plows, and
    some lay wrapped in the loam,
And slept the sleep of the fearless heart that has fought
    for home — for home!

Fought for their homes, at home, they did — but these
    other boys to-day
Fought for the homes of stranger folk three thousand
    miles away;
Fought for the honor of the world, and were not afraid
    to die
In a muddy trench, in a foreign land, and under a foreign
    sky!

They fought on the Marne, at Belleau Wood; they swept
    through the mad Argonne;
Château-Thierry was theirs to take; they took it and
    then surged on;
And now that the fight they fought is won, though they
    lie in a far-off grave,

Their souls come back to the land they loved — the land
    that they *left* to save.

And so, through the damp of the sorry sea, through the
    wreck of the shell-torn plain,
They are coming back to homes they loved — they are
    coming back again!
And light as the wind that sways in the wheat or the
    dust on the broad highway,
They march to their rendezvous with the ones who died
    in the yesterday.

The Torch of Liberty

Thomas Moore

I saw it all in Fancy's glass —
    Herself, the fair, the wild magician,
Who bade this splendid day-dream pass,
    And named this gilded apparition.
'Twas like a torch-race — such as they
    Of Greece performed in ages gone,
When the fleet youths in long array,
    Passed the bright torch triumphant on,
    To catch the coming flame in turn;
I saw, the expectant nation and
    The clear, though struggling, glory burn.
And oh, their joy, as it came near,
    'Twas, in itself, a joy to see;
While fancy whispered in my ear,
    " That torch they pass is Liberty! "

And each, as she received the flame,
    Lighted her altar with its ray;

Then, smiling, to the next who came,
    Speeded it on its sparkling way.
From Albion first, whose ancient shrine
    Was furnished with the flame already,
Columbia caught the boon divine,
    And lit a flame, like Albion's, steady.

Shine, shine forever, glorious flame,
    Divinest gift of gods to men!
From Greece thy earliest splendor came,
    To Greece thy ray returns again.
Take, Freedom, take thy radiant round;
    When dimmed, revive; when lost, return;
Till not a shrine through earth be found
    On which thy glories shall not burn!

Quotations for Independence Day

Ambition, superstition and avarice, those universal torches of war, never illumined an American field of battle. But the permanent principles of sober policy spread through the colonies, aroused the people to assert their rights, and conducted the revolution. Those principles were noble, as they were new and unprecedented in the history of human nations. The majority of a great people, on a subject which they understand, will never act wrong.—*Joel Barlow.*

But from the common versatility of all human destiny, should the prospect hereafter darken, and the clouds of public misfortune thicken to a tempest; should the voice of our country's calamity ever call us to her relief, we swear by the precious memory of the sages who toiled and of the heroes who bled in her defense, that we will prove ourselves not unworthy of the prize which they so dearly purchased; that we will act as the faithful disciples of those who so magnanimously taught us the instructive lesson of republican virtue.— *John Quincy Adams.*

> United States! the ages plead,
>   Present and Past in under-song;
> Go, put your creed into your deed,
>   Nor speak with double tongue.
> Be just at home; then write your scroll
>   Of honor o'er the sea,
> And bid the broad Atlantic roll
>   A ferry of the Free.
>   — *Ralph Waldo Emerson.*

Our Country! In her intercourse with foreign nations, may she always be in the right; but our Country, right or wrong.— *Stephen Decatur.*

The Declaration of Independence is one of the most solemn and memorable professions of political faith that ever emanated from the leading minds of our country. A devout recognition of God and of His overruling Providence pervades the momentous document from beginning to end. God's holy name greets us in the opening paragraph, and is piously invoked in the last sentence of the Declaration; and thus it is, at the same time, the corner-stone and the keystone of this great monument of freedom.— *Cardinal Gibbons.*

May this immense Temple of Freedom ever stand a lesson to oppressors, an example to the oppressed, a sanctuary for the rights of mankind.— *Marquis de Lafayette.*

The great doctrines of the Declaration germinated in the hearts of our fathers, and were developed under the new influences of this wilderness world, by the same subtle mystery which brings forth the rose from the germ of the rose tree. Unconsciously to themselves, the great truths were growing under the new conditions, until like the century plant, they blossomed into the matchless beauty of the

Declaration of Independence, whose fruitage, increased and increasing, we enjoy to-day.— *James A. Garfield.*

We celebrate the return of the day on which our separate national existence was declared,— the day when the momentous experiment was commenced, by which the world and posterity, and we ourselves were to be taught how far a nation of men can be trusted with self government,— how far life, liberty and property are safe and the progress of social improvement is secure, under the influence of laws made by those who are to obey them,— the day when, for the first time in the world, a numerous people was ushered into the family of nations, organized on the political equality of all the citizens.— *Edward Everett.*

The sacred rights of man are not to be rummaged for among old parchments or musty records. They are written as with a sunbeam in the whole volume of human nature by the hand of divinity itself and can never be erased by mortal power.— *Anonymous.*

Whatever may be our fate, be assured, that this Declaration will stand. . . . Through the thick gloom of the present, I see the brightness of the future, as the sun, in heaven. We shall make this a glorious, an immortal day. When we are in our graves our children will honor it. They will celebrate it with thanksgiving, with festivity, with bonfires and illuminations. On its annual return they will shed tears, copious gushing tears, not of subjection and slavery, not of agony and distress, but of exultation, of gratitude and of joy. Sir, before God, I believe the hour is come. My judgment approves this measure and my whole heart is in it. All that I have, and all that I am, and all that I hope, in this life, I am now ready here to stake upon it. And I leave off as I began, that, live or die, survive or perish, I am for the Declaration. It is my living sentiment, and by the blessing of God it shall be my dying sentiment,— *Independence now* and *Independence Forever! — Daniel Webster.*

"Clang! Clang!" the bell of Liberty resounded on, higher and clearer and more joyous, blending in its deep and thrilling vibration, and proclaiming in loud and long accents over all the land this motto that encircled it —" Proclaim liberty throughout the land, unto all the inhabitants thereof." — *J. T. Headley.*

The Declaration of Independence has long been treated as if it were impenetrably sacred. It has been cherished like the Tables of the Law which came straight from the hands of God.— *Barrett Wendell.*

May our land be a land of liberty, the seat of virtue, the asylum of the oppressed, a name and a praise in the whole earth, until the last shock of time shall bury the empires of the world in one common undistinguished ruin! — *Joseph Warren.*

What Patrick Henry meant by liberty, and what subsequent America has meant by liberty, was first and foremost native independence; it was the political freedom of America from all control; from all coercion, from all interference by any power foreign to our own American selves.— *Andrew Wendell.*

The Republican form of government is the arch of triumph that leads to the realization of our high ideals! The Republic, because it has for its foundation, liberty and equality, — because it gives the individual man time and room for free, untrammeled development,— is the highway that leads to the temple of true human dignity.— *Frederick Hecker.*

The men who wrote in the cabin of the *Mayflower* the first charter of freedom, a government of just and equal laws, were a little band of Protestants against every form of injustice and tyranny. The leaven of their principles made possible the Declaration of Independence, liberated the slaves, and founded the free commonwealth which forms the Republic of the United States.— *Chauncey M. Depew.*

Jefferson's superb crystallization of the popular opinion that "all men are created equal, that they are endowed by their Creator with certain inalienable rights, that among these are life, liberty, and the pursuit of happiness" has its force and effect in being the deliberate utterance of the people.— *Chauncey M. Depew.*

The open door of the Republic will invite the oppressed of every land to seek asylum and enter upon the enjoyment of liberty. Impartial justice will stand ready to succor and to aid all who shall appeal from wrong or violence or intimidation. And that grand future of democratic unity will arrive when our people of every lineage and every type shall meet on the plane of equal rights to attest a nationality that will stand out a waymark to the centuries.— *B. Gratz Brown.*

The American Republic was established by the united valor and wisdom of the lovers of liberty from all lands.— *Daniel W. Voorhees.*

The Declaration of Independence is the grandest, the bravest and the profoundest political document that was ever signed by the representatives of the people.— *Robert G. Ingersoll.*

The Puritan principle in its essence is simply individual freedom. From that spring religious liberty and political equality. The free State, the free Church, the free School — these are the triple armor of American nationality, of American security.— *George William Curtiss.*

The new Republic, as it took its place among the powers of the world, proclaimed its faith in the truth and reality and unchangeableness of freedom, virtue and right.— *George Bancroft.*

For years, the celebration of this great holiday has consisted mainly of meaningless noise; but there is a steadily growing sentiment in favor of a more worthy observance of the day, as a time when every loyal American should rejoice in the welfare of his country, and recall with pride the manner in which the Nation was established.— *Anonymous.*

I have never had a feeling politically that did not spring from the sentiments embodied in the Declaration of Independence, which gave liberty, not alone to the people of this country, but to the world in all future time.— *Abraham Lincoln.*

> Amid the stars they sang,
> And the stars heard, and the sea,
> And the sounding aisles of the dim woods rang
> To the anthem of the free.
>
> — Mrs. Hemans.

Even so the wild birds sang on bough and wall
That day the Bell of Independence Hall
Thundered around the world the Word of man,
That day when Liberty began
And mighty hopes were blown on every sea.
But Freedom calls her conscripts now as then —
Calls for heroic men:
It is an endless battle to be free.

— Edwin Markham.

We therefore, the representatives of the United States of America, in General Congress assembled, appealing to the Supreme Judge of the world for the rectitude of our intentions, do, in the name and by the authority of the good people of these colonies, solemnly publish and declare that these United Colonies are, and of right ought to be, FREE AND INDEPENDENT STATES; that they are absolved from all allegiance to the British crown, and that all political connection between them and the state of Great Britain, is and ought to be, totally dissolved; and that, as FREE AND INDEPENDENT STATES, they have full power to levy war, conclude peace, contract alliances, establish commerce, and to do all other acts and things which independent States may of right do. And for the support of this Declaration, with a firm reliance on the protection of Divine Providence, we mutually pledge to each other our lives, our fortunes, and our sacred honor! — *Thomas Jefferson.*

Let us as we assemble on the birthday of the Nation, as we gather upon the green turf, once wet with precious blood — let us devote ourselves to the sacred cause of Constitutional Liberty! Let us abjure the interests and passions which divide the great family of American freemen! Let the rage of party spirit sleep to-day! Let us resolve that our children shall have cause to bless the memory of their fathers as we have cause to bless the memory of ours! — *Edward Everett.*

If you have great talents, industry will improve them; if moderate abilities, industry will supply their deficiencies. Nothing is denied to well-directed labor; nothing is ever to be obtained without it.— *Reynolds.*

LABOR DAY

September —

A bill was passed in Congress in 1894 making the first Monday in September a national holiday. This day has become known as Labor Day. So far as ordinary business is concerned, Congress has no right to create a holiday in the states that have not already approved of it. Congress did merely what was in their power to do to honor the day chosen by organized labor as its special anniversary. The day is now a legal holiday in every state of the Union except one.

Toil

Anonymous

THERE'S a never-dying chorus
Breaking on the human ear;
In the busy town before us,
Voices loud, and deep, and clear.
This is labor's endless ditty;
This is toil's prophetic voice,
Sounding through the town and city,
Bidding human hearts rejoice.

Sweeter than the poet's singing
Is that anthem of the free;
Blither is the anvil's ringing
Than the song of bird or bee.
There's a glory in the rattle
Of the wheels 'mid factory gloom;
Richer than e'er snatched from battle
Or the trophies of the loom.

See the skillful mason raising
Gracefully yon towering pile;
Round the forge and furnace blazing,
Stand the noble men of toil.
They are heroes of the people,
Who the wealth of nations raise;
Every dome, and spire, and steeple
Raise their heads in labor's praise.

Glorious men of truth and labor,
Shepherds of the human fold,
That shall lay the brand and saber
With the barbarous things of old.
Priests and prophets of creation,
Bloodless heroes in the fight,
Toilers for the world's salvation,
Messengers of peace and light.

Speed the plow and speed the harrow;
Peace and plenty send abroad;
Better far the spade and barrow
Than the cannon or the sword.
Each invention, each improvement,
Renders weak oppression's rod;
Every sign and every movement
Brings us nearer truth and God.

Hand of Labor

Lilburn H. Townsend

HAND of labor, hand of might,
Be thou strong in things of right.
Master thou of crafts untold,
Driving them in heat and cold;
Working high and working low,
That the world may brighter grow;
Press, the loom, and traffic great,
Know the drive behind thy weight.

Hand of labor, rude and fine,
Things of earth are mostly thine.
Mines of gold and fields of wheat,
Harbors deep where pennants greet;

Ships of war, canals and locks,
Roads of steel and bridges, docks,
Strain thy sinews day and night.
Be thou strong in things of right.

Mills and shops in clang and roar,
Foundry fires and molten ore;
Sullen mines and heaving seas,
Lands of rocks and timber trees;
Cotton fields as white as snow,
Forges black 'mid flames aglow,
Strain thy sinews day and night,
Be thou strong in things of right.

Hand of labor, great thou art;
Be thou fair, and bear thy part
Like big souls, sincere, intense;
Stoop not low to base offense,
Nor, in heat, forget that men,
Large and small, all kinds and ken,
Have their place and must remain
'Neath the sway of guiding brain.

The Day and the Work

Edwin Markham

(Author of " The Man With the Hoe and other Poems ")

THERE is waiting a work where only his hands can avail;
And so, if he falters, a chord in the music will fail.
He may laugh to the sky, he may lie for an hour in the
  sun;
But he dare not go hence till the labor appointed is done.

To each man is given a marble to carve for the wall:
A stone that is needed to heighten the beauty of all:
And only his soul has the magic to give it a grace:
And only his hands have the cunning to put it in place.

The Thinker

Berton Braley

Back of the beating hammer
　By which the steel is wrought,
Back of the workshop's clamor
　The seeker may find the Thought,
The thought that is ever Master
　Of iron and steam and steel,
That rises above disaster
　And tramples it under heel.

The drudge may fret and tinker
　Or labor with lusty blows,
But back of him stands the Thinker,
　The clear-eyed man who knows;
For into each plow or saber,
　Each piece and part and whole,
Must go the brains of labor,
　Which gives the work a soul.

Back of the motor's humming,
　Back of the bells that sing,
Back of the hammer's drumming,
　Back of the cranes that swing,
There is the Eye which scans them,
　Watching through stress and strain,
There is the Mind which plans them —
　Back of the brawn, the Brain.

Might of the roaring boiler,
  Force of the engine's thrust,
Strength of the sweating toiler,
  Greatly in these we trust,
But back of them stands the schemer,
  The Thinker who drives things through,
Back of the job — The Dreamer
  Who's making the dream come true.

Property is the Fruit of Labor

Abraham Lincoln

PROPERTY is the fruit of labor; property is desirable;
is a positive good in the world.   That some should be rich
shows that others may become rich, and hence is just
encouragement to industry and enterprise.   Let not him
who is houseless pull down the house of another, but let
him work diligently and build one for himself, thus by
example assuring that his own shall be safe from violence
when built.

Blessing of Toil

S. E. Kiser

I BLESS the fates that I may toil,
  I have no wish to waste the day
While others build and others hew
And strive among the chosen few
  That clear obstructions from the way.

I find it good to be among
  The ones whose limbs and hearts are strong,

To earn the comforts I possess,
To try to prove my usefulness
  In helping to push things along.

I do not envy him who sits
  In idleness from morn till night
With nothing more to do than fret
Because he finds it hard to get
  A hearty, healthy appetite.

Work

James Russell Lowell

No man is born into the world whose work
Is not born with him; there is always work
And tools to work withal, for those who will;
And blessed are the horny hands of toil;
  The busy world shoves angrily aside
The man who stands with arms akimbo set,
Until occasion tells him what to do;
And he who waits to have his task marked out,
Shall die and leave his errand unfulfilled.

By permission of, and special arrangement with Houghton Mifflin Co.

The Riveter

Margaret E. Sangster

His hammer falls with rhythmic, Titan grace,
  While beads of moisture stand upon his face;
Beneath the sun he toils, and never dreams
  That he may be a savior of his race.

He only knows the rivets he drives
Must be well placed and firm — and so he strives
   To do the best he can.   And yet his work
It is that safeguards many precious lives.

He does not dream, perhaps, and yet we know
The distance that his well-built ships will go —
   We know the tempests of the angry sea,
The high-flung waves, the stormy winds that blow!

He only knows he has a task, and he
Must do it! So he flings across the sea
   A bridge of ships to meet his Nation's needs,
A bridge that leads to Peace and Liberty.

Labor

Anonymous

Labor is wealth,— in the sea the pearl groweth;
Rich the queen's robe from the frail cocoon floweth;
From the fine acorn the strong forest bloweth;
Temple and statue the marble block hides.

Work for some good, be it ever so slowly;
Cherish some flower, be it ever so lowly;
Labor! — all labor is noble and holy;
Let thy great deed be thy prayer to thy God.

Work

Thomas Carlyle

THERE is a perennial nobleness, and even sacredness, in work. Were a man ever so benighted, or forgetful of his high calling, there is always hope in him who actually and earnestly works; in idleness alone is there perpetual despair. Consider how, even in the meanest sort of labor, the whole soul of a man is composed into real harmony. He bends himself with free valor against his task; and doubt, desire, sorrow, remorse, indignation, despair itself, shrink murmuring, far off into their caves. The glow of labor in him is a purifying fire, wherein all poison is burnt up; and of smoke itself there is made a bright and blessed flame.

Blessed is he who has found his work; let him ask no other blessedness; he has a life purpose. Labor is life. From the heart of the worker rises the celestial force, breathed into him by Almighty God, awakening him to all nobleness, to all knowledge. Hast thou valued patience, courage, openness to light, or readiness to own thy mistakes? In wrestling with the dim, brute powers of Fact, thou wilt continually learn. For every noble work, the possibilities are diffused through immensity — undiscoverable, except to Faith.

Man, son of Heaven! is there not in thine inmost heart a spirit of active method, giving thee no rest till thou unfold it? Complain not. Look up, wearied brother. See thy fellow-workman surviving through eternity — sacred band of immortals!

Labor

Orville Dewey

To some field of labor, mental or manual, every idler should fasten, as a chosen and coveted theater of improvement. But so he is not impelled to do, under the teachings of our imperfect civilization. On the contrary, he sits down, folds his hands, and blesses himself in his idleness. This way of thinking is the heritage of the absurd and unjust feudal system under which serfs labored, and gentlement spent their lives in fighting and feasting. It is time that this opprobrium of toil were done away. Ashamed to toil, art thou? Ashamed of thy dingy work-shop and dusty labor-field; of thy hard hand scarred with service more honorable than that of war; of thy soiled and weather-stained garments, on which Mother Nature has embroidered, midst sun and rain, midst fire and stream, her own heraldic honors? Ashamed of these tokens and titles, and envious of the flaunting robes of imbecile idleness and vanity? It is treason to nature; it is impiety to Heaven; it is breaking Heaven's great ordinance. Toil, I repeat — toil, either of the brain, of the heart, or of the hand, is the only true manhood, the only true nobility.

Do Thy Day's Work

Anonymous

Do thy day's work, my dear,
Though fast and dark the clouds are drifting near;
Though time has little left for hope and very much for
    fear.

Do thy day's work, though now
The hand must falter, and the head must bow,
And far above the failing foot shows the bold mountain
brow.

Yet there is left for us,
Who on the valley's verge stand trembling thus,
A light that lies far in the west — soft, faint, but lum-
inous.
We can give kindly speech
And ready helping hand to all and each,
And patience to the young around by smiling silence
teach.

We can give gentle thought
And charity by life's long lesson taught,
And wisdom, from old faults lived down, by toil and
failure wrought.
We can give love, unmarred
By selfish snatch of happiness; unjarred
By the keen aims of power or joy, that make youth
cold and hard.

And, if gay hearts reject
The gifts we hold, would fain fare on unchecked
On the bright roads that scarcely yield all that young
eyes expect,
Why, do thy day's work still.
The calm, deep founts of love are slow to chill;
And Heaven may yet the harvest yield, the work-worn
hands to fill.

The World Wants Men

Anonymous

THE world wants men, large-hearted, manly men,
Men who shall join its chorus and prolong
   The song of labor and the song of love.

The time wants scholars, scholars who shall shape
The doubtful destiny of dubious years
And land the ark that bears our country's good
   Safe on some peaceful Ararat at last.

The age wants heroes, heroes who shall dare
To struggle in the solid ranks of truth;
To clutch the monster error by the throat;
To bear opinion to a loftier seat;
To blot the era of oppression out
   And lead a universal freedom in.

And Heaven wants souls; fresh and capacious souls
To taste its rapture and expand like flowers
Beneath the glory of the central Sun.
It wants fresh souls — not lean and shriveled ones —
   It wants fresh souls, my brother, give it thine.

If thou indeed wilt be a hero and wilt strive
To help thy fellow and exalt thyself,
Thy feet at last shall stand on jasper floors,
Thy heart shall seem a thousand hearts,
Each single heart with myriad raptures filled,
Whilst thou shall sit with princes and kings,
   Rich in the jewel of a ransomed soul.

Work

Angela Morgan

WORK!
Thank God for the might of it,
The ardor, the urge, the delight of it;
Work that springs from the heart's desire,
Setting the brain and the soul on fire —
Oh, what is so good as the heat of it,
And what is so glad as the beat of it,
And what is so kind as the stern command,
Challenging brain and heart and hand?

Work!
Thank God for the pride of it,
For the beautiful, conquering tide of it,
Sweeping the life in its furious flood,
Thrilling the arteries, cleansing the blood,
Mastering stupor and dull despair,
Moving the dreamer to do and dare;
Oh, what is so good as the urge of it,
And what is so glad as the surge of it,
And what is so strong as the summons deep,
Rousing the torpid soul from sleep?

Work!
Thank God for the pace of it,
For the terrible, keen swift race of it;
Fiery steeds in full control,
Nostrils a-quiver to greet the goal.
Work, the Power that drives behind,
Guiding the purposes, taming the mind,
Holding the runaway wishes back,

Reining the will to one steady track,
Speeding the energies faster, faster,
Triumphing over disaster.
Oh, what is so good as the pain of it,
And what is so great as the gain of it?
And what is so kind as the cruel goad,
Forcing us on through the rugged road?

Work!
Thank God for the swing of it,
For the clamoring, hammering ring of it,
Passion of labor daily hurled
On the mighty anvils of the world.
Oh, what is so fierce as the flame of it?
And what is so huge as the aim of it?
Thundering on through dearth and doubt,
Calling the plan of the Maker out.
Work, the Titan! Work, the friend,
Shaping the earth to a glorious end,
Draining the swamps and blasting the hills,
Doing whatever the Spirit wills —
Rending a continent apart,
To answer the dream of the Master heart;
Thank God for a world where none may shirk —
Thank God for the splendor of work!

From the *Outlook*.

The World is Waiting For You

S. S. Calkins

THE world is waiting for you, young man,
  If your purpose is strong and true;
If out of your treasures of mind and heart,
  You can bring things old and new;
If you know the truth that makes men free,
  And with skill can bring it to view,
The world is waiting for you, young man,
  The world is waiting for you.

There are treasures of mountain and treasures of sea,
  And harvest of valley and plain,
That Industry, Knowledge and Skill can secure,
  While Ignorance wishes in vain.
To scatter the lightning and harness the storm,
  Is a power that is wielded by few;
If you have the nerve and the skill, young man,
  The world is waiting for you.

Of the idle and brainless the world has enough —
  Who eat what they never have earned;
Who hate the pure stream from the fountain of truth,
  And wisdom and knowledge have spurned.
But patience and purpose which know no defeat,
  And genius like gems bright and true,
Will bless all mankind with their love, life and light,—
  The world is waiting for you.

Then awake, O, young man, from the stupor of doubt,
  And prepare for the battle of life;

Be the fire of the forge, or be anvil or sledge,—
  But win or go down in the strife!
Can you stand though the world into ruin should rock?
  Can you conquer with many or few?
Then the world is waiting for you, young man,
  The world is waiting for you.

Find a Way

John G. Saxe

It was a noble Roman,
  In Rome's imperial day,
Who heard a coward croaker,
  Before the castle, say,
" They're safe in such a fortress;
  There is no way to shake it!"
" On! On!" exclaimed the hero,
  " I'll find a way, or make it!"

Is Fame your aspiration?
  Her path is steep and high;
In vain you seek her temple,
  Content to gaze and sigh:
The shining throne is waiting,
  But he alone can take it,
Who says, with Roman firmness,
  " I'll find a way, or make it!"

Is Learning your ambition?
  There is no royal road;
Alike the peer and peasant
  Must climb to her abode;

Who feels the thirst for knowledge
   In Helicon may slake it,
If he has still the Roman will,
   To " find a way, or make it ! "

Are Riches worth the getting?
   They must be bravely sought;
With wishing and with fretting,
   The boon can not be bought;
To all the prize is open,
   But only he can take it,
Who says, with Roman courage,
   " I'LL FIND A WAY, OR MAKE IT ! "

The Song of Labor

Ninette M. Lowater

I SING the song of the workman,
The joy of the man whose hand
Leaps to fulfill with practised skill
The keen, sure brain's demand,
Who knows the thrill of creation,
Who stands with the Lord as one —
Sees what was wrought from hidden thought,
And can say of his work, " Well done! "

Others may seek for rank and wealth,
And search the wide world through —
He knows the deep where grand thoughts sleep,
Which Tubal Cain once knew;
Beauty may lie in a woman's eye,
And dwell on her lips so sweet —
It lives as well in the engine's swell,
And the piston's throbbing beat.

The arch which defies the river's flood,
And holds its waves in check,
Is fair as the line where tresses twine,
Or the curve of a snowy neck;
And he who can feel such beauty's power,
And bid it live and move,
Knows a deeper bliss than a maiden's kiss
Can give to the heart of love.

Some must lie soft and feed daintily,
Or the soul in them makes moan;
But little he heeds who finds his needs
In the maker's joy alone.
Sorrow and pain may come to him,—
They surely come to all,—
But ever he feels a strength that steels
His heart to the shafts that fall.

He gladly greets the coming years;
They bring him added skill.
He feels no ruth for the loss of youth;
His goal is nearer still;
And only this he asks of fate:
That he may keep his dower
Of strength, and will, and labor's skill
Unto his life's last hour.

The Man With the Hoe

'Edwin Markham

"God created man in his own image, in the image of God created he him."

Bowed by the weight of centuries, he leans
Upon his hoe and gazes on the ground,
The emptiness of ages in his face,
And on his back the burden of the world.
Who made him dead to rapture and despair,
A thing that grieves not and that never hopes,
Stolid and stunned, a brother to the ox?
Who loosened and let down this brutal jaw?
Whose was the hand that slanted back this brow?
Whose breath blew out the light within this brain?

Is this the Thing the Lord God made and gave
To have dominion over sea and land;
To trace the stars and search the heavens for power;
To feel the passion of Eternity?
Is this the Dream He dreamed who shaped the suns
And pillared the blue firmament with light?
Down all the stretch of Hell to its last gulf
There is no shape more terrible than this —
More tongued with censure of the world's blind greed —
More filled with signs and portents for the soul —
More fraught with menace to the universe.

What gulfs between him and the seraphim!
Slave of the wheel of labor; what to him
Are Plato and the swing of Pleiades?
What the long reaches of the peaks of song,

The rift of dawn, the reddening of the rose?
Through this dread shape the suffering ages look;
Time's tragedy is in that aching stoop;
Through this dread shape humanity, betrayed,
Plundered, profaned and disinherited,
Cries protest to the Judges of the World —
A protest that is also prophecy.

O masters, lords and rulers in all lands,
Is this the handiwork you give to God,
This monstrous thing distorted and soul-quenched?
How will you ever straighten up this shape;
Touch it again with immortality;
Give back the upward looking and the light;
Rebuild it in the music and the dream;
Make right the immemorial infamies;
Perfidious wrongs, immedicable woes?

O masters, lords and rulers in all lands,
How will the Future reckon with this Man?
How answer his brute question in that hour
When whirlwinds of rebellion shake the world?
How will it be with kingdoms and with kings —
With those who shaped him to the thing he is —
When this dumb Terror shall reply to God,
After the silence of the centuries?

Quotations for Labor Day

A man perfects himself by working.— *Carlyle.*

A man's task is always light if his heart is light.— *Lew Wallace.*

Grumblers never work, and workers never grumble.— *Spurgeon.*

He is greatest who makes all that is possible out of himself. There is no power within the heavens above that would, or in the earth beneath that can, ever defeat a combination of integrity and industry.— *Robert G. Cousins.*

> Toil, and the arm grows stronger;
> Sluggards are ever weak.
> Toil, and the earth gives forth
> Riches to those that seek.
> — *James P. Bloomfield.*

The most profitable and praiseworthy genius in the world is untiring industry.— *E. L. Magoon.*

> Work while you work, play while you play;
> This is the way to be cheerful and gay.
> All that you do, do with your might;
> Things done by halves are never done right.
>
> One thing at a time, and that done well,
> Is a very good rule, as many can tell;
> Moments are useless, trifled away;
> So work while you work, and play while you play.
> — *Miss A. D. Stoddart.*

Toil, I repeat — toil either of the brain, or of the heart, or of the hand, is the only true manhood, the only true nobility.— *Orville Dewey.*

Beautiful eyes are those that show
Beautiful thoughts that burn below;
Beautiful lips are those whose words
Leap from the heart like songs of birds;
Beautiful hands are those that do
Work that is earnest, brave and true,
Moment by moment the whole day through.

— Selected.

To be truly and really independent is to support ourselves by our own exertions.— *Jane Porter.*

We should so live and labor in our own time that what came to us as seed may go to the next generation as blossom, and that what came to us as blossom may go to them as fruit. This is what we mean by progress.— *Selected.*

Some temptations come to the industrious, but all temptations attack the idle.— *Spurgeon.*

The world is crowded on its lower floor, but higher up, for centuries to come, there will still remain a niche for each piece of honest work.— *Jordan.*

No abilities, however splendid, can command success without intense labor and persevering application.— *Selected.*

All true work is sacred; in all true work, were it not true hand-labor, there is something of divineness. Labor, wide as the earth, has its summit in heaven.— *Carlyle.*

No man is born into the world whose work
Is not born with him; there is always work,
And tools to work withal, for those who will;
And blessed are the horny hands of toil!

— Lowell.

Do not, then, stand idly waiting
　For some greater work to do;
Fortune is a lazy goddess,
　She will never come to you.

Go and toil in any vineyard,
  Do not fear to do or dare,
If you want a field of labor,
  You can find it anywhere.

— Selected.

Self-ease is pain; thy only rest
Is labor for a worthy end.
Self-offering is a triumph won;
And each good thought or action moves
The dark world nearer to the sun.

— Whittier.

Set yourself earnestly to see what you were made to do,
and then set yourself earnestly to do it.— *Phillips Brooks.*

If the power to do hard work is not talent, it is the best
possible substitute for it.— *James A. Garfield.*

I cannot too much impress upon your mind that labor is
the condition which God has imposed on us in every station
of life; there is nothing worth having that can be had
without it. As for knowledge, it can no more be planted
in the human mind without labor than a field of wheat can
be produced without the previous use of the plow. If we
neglect our spring, our summer will be useless and con-
temptible, our harvest will be chaff and the winter of our
old age unrespected and desolate.— *Sir Walter Scott.*

I was born an American; I live an American; I shall die an American; and I intend to perform the duties incumbent upon me in that character to the end of my career. Let the consequences be what they will. No man can suffer too much, and no man can fall too soon, if he suffer, or if he fall, in the defense of the liberties and constitution of his country.— *Daniel Webster.*

CONSTITUTION DAY

September 17

The 17th of September is not a legal holiday in any of the states but it is observed in the schools by the recitation of appropriate pieces and selections. It was on September 17th, 1787, that George Washington, President of the Constitutional Convention, signed the Constitution which had just been drawn up after four months of stormy debate between those who wanted more power given to the states. In a little more than half a year after this date the requisite number of nine states had ratified the agreement, and the Constitution became the fundamental law of the land.

Preamble to the Constitution of the United States of America

— WE, the people of the United States, in order to form a more perfect union, establish justice, insure domestic tranquillity, provide for the common defense, promote the general welfare, and secure the blessings of liberty to ourselves and our posterity, do ordain and establish this Constitution.

The Pilgrim Fathers

John Boyle O'Reilly

HERE, on this rock, and on this sterile soil,
Began the kingdom, not of kings, but men;
Began the making of the world again.
Here centuries sank, and from the hither brink,
A new world reached and raised an old world link,
    When English hands, by wider vision taught,
    Threw down the feudal bars the Normans brought
And here revived, in spite of sword and stake,
Their ancient freedom of the Wapentake;
    Here struck the see — the Pilgrim's roofless town,
Where equal rights and equal bonds were set;
Where all the people, equal franchised, met;
    Where doom was writ of privilege and crown;
    Where human breath blew all the idols down;
Where crests were naught, where vulture flags were
      furled,
And common men began to own the world!

America the Beautiful

Katharine Lee Bates

O BEAUTIFUL for spacious skies,
 For amber waves of grain,
For purple mountain majesties
 Above the fruited plain!
  America! America!
 God shed His grace on thee
And crown thy good with brotherhood
  From sea to shining sea!

O beautiful for pilgrim feet,
 Whose stern, impassioned stress
A thoroughfare for freedom beat
 Across the wilderness!
  America! America!
 God mend thine every flaw,
Confirm thy soul in self-control,
  Thy liberty in law!

O beautiful for heroes proved
 In liberating strife,
Who more than self their country loved,
 And mercy more than life!
  America! America!
 May God thy gold refine
Till all success be nobleness
 And every gain divine!

O beautiful for patriot dream
 That sees beyond the years

Thine alabaster cities gleam
  Undimmed by human tears
    America! America!
  God shed His grace on thee
And crown thy good with brotherhood
  From sea to shining sea!

America

S. F. Smith, LL.D.

My country, 'tis of thee,
Sweet land of liberty,
  Of thee I sing;
Land where my fathers died,
Land of the pilgrim's pride;
From every mountain side,
  Let freedom ring.

My native country thee,
Land of the noble free,
  Thy name I love;
I love thy rocks and rills,
Thy woods and templed hills;
My heart with rapture thrills
  Like that above.

Let music swell the breeze,
And ring from all the trees
  Sweet freedom's song;
Let mortal tongues awake,
Let all that breathe partake,
Let rocks their silence break —
  The sound prolong.

Our fathers' God to Thee,
Author of Liberty,
   To Thee we sing;
Long may our land be bright
With freedom's holy light;
Protect us by Thy might,
   Great God, our King!

America

Florence Earle Coates

PATIENT she is — long-suffering, our Land;
   Wise with the strength of one whose soul in calm
Weighs and considers, and would understand
   Ere it gives way to anger: fearing wrong
Of her own doing more than any planned
   Against her peace by others deemed more strong.

Mother of many children alien born,
   Whom she has gathered into her kind arms —
Safe-guarding most the weakest, most forlorn —
   The mother's patience she has learned to know,
Which passes trifles by with smiling scorn —
   The mother's hopefulness, to anger slow.

Yet, oh, beware! nor, over-bold, presume
   Upon a gentleness enlinked with Power!
Her torch still burns, to kindle or consume,
   And 'gainst the time when she must prove her might,
Vast energy is stored in her soul's room —
   Undreamed of strength to battle for the Right!

Americans All

Minna Irving

FROM the moors and the tors of old England,
　The wild Irish glens and the bogs,
The banks and the braes of the Highlands,
　And Holland the country of fogs.
From the Rhine and the Seine and the Tiber,
　And the Alps where the Yodelers call,
They come o'er the stormy Atlantic —
　Americans all.

For here on the rim of the sunset
　The land is a melting-pot vast,
And into it goes every stranger
　Regardless of color or caste.
The immigrant boy with his bundle,
　The immigrant girl with her shawl,
Emerge from the caldron of Nations —
　Americans all.

The tools of new labors await them,
　Each a wand full of magic to wield
In the charming of gold from the highway,
　The shop and the mill and the field.
And Fortune to some of them beckons
　From the windows of skyscrapers tall;
Prosperous, happy — behold them!
　Americans all.

So when on the horizon rises
　A war-cloud to threaten the land,
With Liberty's native-born children

Shoulder to shoulder they stand,
For America ready to battle,
  For America ready to fall,
Not Russians nor Swedes nor Italians —
  Americans All.

There is a Land

James Montgomery

THERE is a land, of every land the pride,
Beloved by Heaven o'er all the world beside;
Where brighter suns dispense serener light,
And milder moons imparadise the night;
A land of beauty, virtue, valor, truth,
Time-tutored age, and love-exalted youth.
Where shall that land, that spot of earth be found?
Art thou a man? a patriot? look around!
Oh! thou shalt find, howe'er thy footsteps roam,
That land thy country, and that spot thy home.

Our Native Land

C. T. Brooks

GOD bless our native land!
Firm may she ever stand,
  Through storm and night:
When the wild tempests rave,
Ruler of wind and wave,
Do Thou our country save
  By Thy great might!

For her our prayers shall rise
To God, above the skies;
   On Him we wait:
Thou who art ever nigh,
Guarding the watchful eye,
To Thee aloud we cry,
   " God save the State! "

My Country

(A Patriotic Creed for Americans)

Dr. Frank Crane

I AM an American.

I love my country because it stands for liberty and against all forms of slavery, tyranny, and unjust privilege.

I love my country because it is a democracy, where the people govern themselves, and there is no hereditary class to rule them.

I love my country because the only use it has for an army and navy is to defend itself from unjust attack and to protect its citizens.

I love my country because it asks nothing for itself it would not ask for all humanity.

I love my country because it is the land of opportunity; the way to success is open to every person, no matter what his birth or circumstances.

I love my country because every child in it can get an education free in its public schools and more money is spent on training children here than in any other country.

I love my country because women are respected and honored.

I love my country because we have free speech and a free press.

I love my country because it interferes with no person's religion.

I love my country because its people are industrious, energetic, independent, friendly and have a sense of humor.

I love my country because its heroes are such characters as George Washington and Abraham Lincoln, who loved to serve and not to rule.

I will serve my country in any way I can. I will strive to be a good citizen, and will not do anything nor take part in anything that may wrong the public. I wish to live for my country.

IF NEED BE, I WILL DIE FOR MY COUNTRY.

Copyright, by Dr. Frank Crane.

What Constitutes a State

Sir William Jones

WHAT constitutes a state?
Not high-raised battlements or labored mound,
Thick wall or moated gate;
Not cities proud with spires and turrets crowned;
Not bays and broad-armed ports,
Where, laughing at the storm, rich navies ride;
Not starred and spangled courts,
Where low-browed baseness wafts perfume to pride.
No! *Men,* high-minded *men* —
With powers as far above dull brutes endued,
In forest, brake, or den,
As beasts, excel cold rocks and brambles rude;

Men who their duties know;
And know their rights, and knowing, dare maintain,
Prevent the long-aimed blow,
And crush the tyrant while they rend the chain,
These constitute a state;
And sovereign law, that state's collected will,
O'er thrones and globes elate,
Sits empress, crowning good, repressing ill.

Hail, Columbia

John Hopkinson

HAIL Columbia! happy land,
Hail ye heroes, heav'n born band,
Who fought and bled in freedom's cause,
And when the storm of life was gone
Enjoyed the peace your valor won.
Let independence be our boast
Ever mindful what it cost,
Ever grateful for the prize;
Let its altar reach the skies.

Immortal patriots, rise once more,
Defend your rights, defend your shore,
Let no rude foe with impious hands
Invade the shrine where sacred lies
Of toil and blood the well earned prize.
While off'ring peace sincere and just
In heav'n we place a manly trust
That truth and justice will prevail
And ev'ry scheme of bondage fail.

Sound, sound the trump of fame;
Let our own Washington's great name
Ring thro' the world with loud applause;
Let ev'ry clime to freedom dear,
Listen with a joyful ear.
With equal skill, with God-like power
He governs in the fearful hour
Of horrid war, or guides with ease
The happier times of honest peace.

Behold! the chief who now commands,
Once more, to serve his country stand,
The rock on which the storm will beat,
But, sound in virtue, firm and true,
His hopes are fixed on heav'n and you.
When hope was sinking in dismay,
When gloom obscured Columbia's day,
His steady mind from changes free,
Resolved on death or liberty.

CHORUS

Firm, united let us be,
Rallying round our liberty.
As a band of brothers joined
Peace and safety we shall find.

Hymn of the New World

Percy MacKaye

A STAR — a star in the west!
  Out of the wave it rose:
And it led us forth on a world-far quest;
Where the mesas scorched and the moorlands froze.

It lured us without rest:
　With yearning, yearning — ah!
It sang (as it beckoned us)
A music vast, adventurous —
　　　　America!

A star — a star in the night!
　Out of our hearts it dawned!
And it poured within its wonderful light;
Where our hovels gloomed and our hunger spawned
　It healed our passionate blight:
　And burning, burning — ah!
It clanged (as it kindled us)
Of a freedom proud and perilous —
　　　　America!

A star — a star in the dawn!
　Bright from God's brow it gleams!
Like a morning star in ages gone
With hallowed song its holy beams
　Urge us forever on:
　For chanting, chanting — ah!
It builds (as it blesses us)
A union strong, harmonious —
　　　　America!

Quotations for Constitution Day

With malice toward none, with charity for all, with firmness in the right, as God gives us to see the right, let us strive on to finish the work we are in, to bind up the nation's wounds, to care for him who shall have borne the battle, and for his widow and his orphans — to do all which may achieve and cherish just and lasting peace among ourselves and with all nations.— *Abraham Lincoln.*

A man's country is not a certain area of land, but it is a principle, and patriotism is loyalty to that principle.— *George William Curtis.*

Observe good faith and justice toward all nations, cultivate peace and harmony with all. Religion and morality enjoin this conduct; and can it be that good policy does not equally enjoin it? Can it be that Providence has not connected the permanent felicity of a nation with its virtue? The experiment, at least, is recommended by every sentiment which ennobles human nature.— *George Washington.*

What is it to be an American? Putting aside all the outer shows of dress and manners, social customs and physical peculiarities, is it not to believe in America and in the American people? Is it not to have an abiding and moving faith in the future and in the destiny of America? — something above and beyond the patriotism and love which every man whose soul is not dead within him feels toward the land of his birth? Is it not to be national, and not sectional, independent and not colonial? Is it not to have a high conception of what this great new country should be, and to follow out that ideal with loyalty and truth? — *Henry Cabot Lodge.*

Have we not learned that not stocks nor bonds nor stately houses nor lands nor the product of the mill is our country? It is a spiritual thought that is in our minds. It is the flag and what it stands for. It is its glorious history. It is the fireside and the home. It is the high thoughts that are in the heart, born of the inspiration which comes by the stories of their fathers, the martyrs to liberty; it is the graveyards into which our careful country has gathered the unconscious dust of those who have died. Here, in these things, is that which we love and call our country, rather than in anything that can be touched or handled.— *Benjamin Harrison.*

How shall those who practice election frauds recover that respect for the sanctity of the ballot which is the first condition and obligation of good citizenship? The man who has come to regard the ballot box as a juggler's hat has renounced his allegiance.— *Benjamin Harrison.*

No other people have a government more worthy of their respect and love, or a land so magnificent in extent, so pleasant to look upon, and so full of generous suggestion to enterprise and labor. God has placed upon our head a diadem, and has laid at our feet power and wealth beyond definition or calculation. But we must not forget that we take these gifts upon the condition that justice and mercy shall hold the reins of power, and that the upward avenues of hope shall be free to all the people.— *Benjamin Harrison.*

Who compose my nation and what constitutes my country? It is not so much land and water. They would remain ever the same, though an alien race occupied the soil; there would be the same green hills and the same sweet valleys, the same ranges of mountains, and the same lakes and rivers; but all these combined do not make up my country. That word "country" comprehends within itself places and people and all that history, tradition, language, manners, social culture, and civil policy have associated with them. This wonderful combination of State and nation, which binds me to both by indissoluble ties, enters into the idea of my country. Its name is the United States of America. — *David Dudley Field.*

Our arsenals and our armories ought to be kept filled with every weapon and munition of war and every vulnerable point on the coast ought to be fortified. But while we act on the maxim —" In peace prepare for war," let us also remember that the best preparation for war is peace. This swells your numbers; this augments your means; this knits the sinews of your strength; this covers you all over with a panoply of might; and then if war must come in a just cause, no power on earth — no sir, not all combined can send forth an adversary from whose encounter you need shrink.— *Edward Everett.*

No progress which did not lift all, ever lifted any. If we let the poisons of filthy diseases percolate through the hovels of the poor, Death knocks at the palace gates. If we leave to the greater horrors of ignorance any portion of our race, the consequences of ignorance strike us all, and there is no escape. We must all move, but we must all keep together. It is only when the rear-guard comes up that the vanguard can go on.— *Thomas B. Reed.*

Wars and sieges pass away and great intellectual efforts cease to stir our hearts, but the man who sacrifices himself for his fellows lives forever.— *Thomas B. Reed.*

In our age there can be no peace that is not honorable; there can be no war that is not dishonorable. The true honor of a nation is to be found only in deeds of justice and in the happiness of its people, all of which are inconsistent with war.— *Charles Sumner.*

The love of country is more powerful than reason itself. — *Ovid.*

This era is distinguished by free representative governments, by entire religious liberty, by improved systems of national intercourse, by a newly awakened and unconquerable spirit of free inquiry, and by a diffusion of knowledge through the community, such as has been before altogether unknown and unheard of. America, America, our country, fellow citizens, our own dear native land, is inseparably connected, fast bound up in the fortune and by fate, with these great interests. If they fall, we fall with them; if they stand, it will be because we have maintained them.— *Daniel Webster* .

By the side of all antagonisms, higher than they, stronger than they, there rises colossal the fine sweet spirit of nationality,— the nationality of America.— *Rufus Choate.*

If there be on earth one nation more than another whose institutions must draw their life-blood from the individual purity of its citizens, that nation is our own.— *Charles Sprague.*

Where public sentiment is the absolute lever that moves the political world, the purity of the people, is the rock of political safety.— *Charles Sprague.*

> O beautiful my country! Ours once more!
> Smoothing thy gold of war-dishevelled hair,
>   And letting thy set lips,
>   Freed from wrath's pale eclipse,
> The rosy edges of thy smile lay bare,
> What words divine of love or of poet
> Could tell our love or make thee know it,
> Among the nations bright beyond compare.
> What were our lives without thee?
> What all our lives to save thee?
> We reck not what we gave thee;
> We will not dare to doubt thee;
> But ask whatever else, and we will dare.
>   — *James Russell Lowell.*

I am not accustomed to the use of language of eulogy. I have never studied the art of paying compliments to women; but I must say that if all that has been said by orators and poets since the creation of the world in praise of women were applied to the women of America, it would not do them justice for their conduct during the war. I will close by saying, God bless the women of America! — *Abraham Lincoln.*

History describes upon none of its pages such a scene. Other governments had grown up under circumstances whose imperious pressure gave them their peculiar forms and they had been modified from time to time, to keep pace with an advancing civilization; but here was a government created by men emancipated from all foreign influence, and who, in their deliberations, acknowledged no supreme authority but that of God.

States already republican and independent were formed into a confederation, and the great principles of the Government were embodied in a Constitution.— *H. W. Hilliard.*

This Union cannot expire as the snow melts from the rock, or a star disappears from the firmament. When it falls, the crash will be heard in all lands. Wherever the winds of heaven go, that will go, bearing sorrow and dismay to millions of stricken hearts; for the subversion of this Government will render the cause of constitutional liberty hopeless throughout the world. What nation can govern itself, if this nation cannot? — *Henry A. Boardman.*

As far as I can see, the American Constitution is the most wonderful work ever struck off at one time by the brain and purpose of man.— *William E. Gladstone.*

Government is a trust, and the officers of the government are trustees; and both the trust and the trustees are created for the benefit of the people.— *Henry Clay.*

Government has no right to control individual liberty, beyond what is necessary to the safety and well-being of society.— *John C. Calhoun.*

I believe this the strongest government on earth. I believe it the only one where every man, at the call of the

law, would fly to the standard of the law, and would meet
invasions of public order, as his own personal concern.—
Thomas Jefferson.

Our institutions are but the hearts, intelligence and conscience of the American people, and their permanence de-
pends upon the quality of American manhood.— *Hon. Charles
T. Saxton.*

Let every American, every lover of liberty, every well-
wisher to his posterity, swear by the blood of the Revolution never to violate in the least particular the laws of the
country and never to tolerate their violation. . . . Let every
man remember that to violate the law is to trample on the
blood of his father, and to tear the charter of his own
and his children's liberty. Let reverence for the law be
breathed by every American mother to the lisping babe that
prattles on her lap; let it be taught in schools, in seminaries,
and in colleges; let it be written in primers, spelling-books
and in almanacs; let it be preached from the pulpit, proclaimed from legislative halls, and enforced in courts of
justice. And, in short, let it become the political religion
of the nation, and let the old and young, the rich and the
poor, the grave and the gay of all sexes and tongues and
colors and conditions sacrifice unceasingly upon its altars.
— *Abraham Lincoln.*

The Constitution was framed by a group of men such as
never had met before in this world, not that there were not
as good, as patriotic, as able men in other countries; but
these men had become familiar with the practical working
of free self-government during one hundred and fifty years
of colonial life.

Thank Heaven, those millions of young men who went
abroad to fight for their country have come back better
patriots, more fitted for the duty of citizenship, more determined to preserve our liberty and peace than ever before.
Thank Heaven, the spirit of the people of the United States

awakened by the trials and sacrifices of these recent years, is more ready than ever since the earliest days to do whatever their country needs for the preservation of its institutions. We must be vigilant and we must be earnest — but we shall be, and we shall preserve for the generation to come, and for the peace and blessing of our children and children's children, that liberty and order which this Constitution has given to us beyond all other people of this or any other time.— *Elihu Root.*

The fame of Columbus is not local or limited. It does not belong to any single country or people. It is the proud possession of the whole civilized world. In all the transactions of history there is no act which for vastness and performance can be compared with the discovery of the continent of America, " the like of which was never done by any man in ancient or in later times."— *James Grant Wilson.*

COLUMBUS DAY

October 12

Columbus Day has been made a legal holiday in the greater majority of the States. The 12th of October is not the anniversary of the birth of Christopher Columbus (as most people suppose) but it is the anniversary of his discovery of the first land of the New World, October 12, 1492. Columbus was born in 1436, the exact date being uncertain.

Columbus

Joaquin Miller

BEHIND him lay the gray Azores,
  Behind, the Gates of Hercules;
Before him not the ghost of shores;
  Before him only shoreless seas.
The good mate said, " Now must we pray,
  For lo! the very stars are gone.
Brave Adm'r'l, speak; what shall I say?"
  " Why, say, ' Sail on! sail on! and on!'"

" My men grow mutinous day by day;
  My men grow ghastly wan and weak."
The stout mate thought of home; a spray
  Of salt wave washed his swarthy cheek.
" What shall I say, brave Adm'r'l, say,
  If we sight naught but seas at dawn?"
" Why, you shall say at break of day:
  ' Sail on! sail on! and on!'"

They sailed and sailed, as winds might blow,
  Until at last the blanched mate said:
" Why, now not even God would know
  Should I and all my men fall dead.
These very winds forget their way,
  For God from these dread seas is gone.
Now speak, brave Adm'r'l; speak and say —"
  He said: " Sail on! sail on! and on!"

They sailed. They sailed. Then spake the mate:
  "This mad sea shows his teeth to-night.
He curls his lip, he lies in wait,
  With lifted teeth as if to bite!
Brave Adm'r'l, say but one good word:
  What shall we do when hope is gone?"
The words leaped like a leaping sword:
  "Sail on! sail on! sail on! and on!"

Then, pale and worn, he kept his deck
  And peered through darkness. Ah, that night
Of all dark nights! And then a speck —
  A light! a light! a light! a light!
It grew, a starlight flag unfurled!
  It grew to be Time's burst of dawn.
He gained a world; he gave that world
  Its grandest lesson: "On! sail on!"

Immortal Morn

Hezekiah Butterworth

IMMORTAL morn, all hail!
  That saw Columbus sail
    By Faith alone!
The skies before him bowed,
Back rolled the ocean proud,
And every lifting cloud
  With glory shone.

Fair science then was born,
On that celestial morn,
  Faith dared the sea;
Triumphant over foes

Then Truth immortal rose,
New heavens to disclose,
 And earth to free.

Strong Freedom then came forth,
To liberate the earth
 And crown the right;
So walked the pilot bold
Upon the sea of gold,
And darkness backward rolled,
 And there was light.

The Boy Columbus

Anonymous

" 'Tis a wonderful story," I hear you say,
" How he struggled and worked and plead and prayed,
And faced every danger undismayed,
With a will that would neither break nor bend,
And discovered a new world in the end —
But what does it teach to a boy of today?
All the worlds are discovered, you know of course,
All the rivers are traced to their utmost source:
There is nothing left for a boy to find,
 If he had ever so much a mind
 To become a discoverer famous;
And if we'd much rather read a book
About someone else, and the risks he took,
 Why nobody, surely, can blame us."

So you think all the worlds are discovered now;
All the lands have been charted and sailed about,
Their mountains climbed, their secrets found out;

All the seas have been sailed, and their currents known —
To the uttermost isles the winds have blown
They have carried a venturing prow?
Yet there lie all about us new worlds, everywhere,
That await their discoverer's footfall; spread fair
Are electrical worlds that no eye has yet seen,
And mechanical worlds that lie hidden serene
  And await their Columbus securely.
There are new worlds in Science and new worlds in Art,
And the boy who will work with his head and his heart
  Will discover his new world surely.

Columbus

James Montgomery

LONG lay the ocean-paths from man concealed;
Light came from heaven,— the magnet was revealed,
A surer star to guide the seaman's eye
Than the pale glory of the northern sky;
Alike ordained to shine by night and day,
Through calm and tempest, with unsetting ray;
Where'er the mountains rise, the billows roll,
Still with strong impulse turning to the pole,
True as the sun is to the morning true,
Though light as film, and trembling as the dew.

Columbus Day

Alfred Tennyson

Do you wonder to see him in chains
Whom once the King rose from his throne to greet?
At Barcelona — the city decked herself
To meet me, roared my name; the King and Queen

Bade me be seated, speak, and tell them all
The story of my voyage, and while I spoke
The crowd's roar fell,
And when I ceased to speak, the King and Queen
Sank from their thrones, and melted into tears,
And knelt, and lifted hand and voice
In praise to God who led me thro' the waste.

And now you see me in chains!
Chains for him who gave a new heaven, a new earth,
Gave glory and more empire to the Kings
Of Spain than did all their battles! Chains for him
Who pushed his prows into the setting sun,
And made West East, and sail'd into the Dragon's mouth,
And came upon the Mountain of the World,
And saw the rivers fall from Paradise!

Eighteen long years of waste, seven in your Spain,
Lost, showing courts and King a truth,— the earth a
    sphere.
At Salamanca we fronted the learning of all Spain,
All their cosmogonies, their astronomies;
No guesswork! I was certain of my goal;
At last their Highnesses were half-assured this earth
    might be a sphere.
Last night a dream I had — I sail'd
On my first voyage, harass'd by the frights
Of my first crew, their curses and their groans.
The compass, like an old friend false at last
In our most need, appall'd them, and the wind
Still westward, and the weedy seas — at length
The landbird, and the branch with berries on it,
The carven staff — and at last the light, the light on Sal-
    vador.

All glory to God!
I have accomplished what I came to do.
I pray you tell King Ferdinand
That I am loyal to him even unto death.

The Return of Columbus to Spain

Don Gomez: His Secretary

Time: March, 1493.
Place: The office of Don Gomez.

Don Gomez: What! What is this you tell me? Columbus has returned? He crossed the western ocean and has returned alive? Impossible!

Secretary: It is even so, Don Gomez. A messenger arrived at the palace an hour ago. Columbus has landed and the news is spreading. All Spain will soon be wild with excitement.

Don Gomez: Oh, it is a trick! It must be a trick.

Secretary: But Columbus has brought home the proofs of his visit — gold and precious stones, strange plants and animals. He has brought also some of the strange people that he found — copper-colored men with straight black hair.

Don Gomez: Still I say it is a trick. He has been sailing along the coast of Africa and has picked up a few things which he pretends are proofs of his discovery.

Secretary: But all his sailors tell the same story.

Don Gomez: We shall see, we shall see. A plain matter-of-fact man, such as I am, is not taken in by such a ridiculous story. We shall find out that Columbus has discovered nothing at all.

Secretary: The king and queen have given orders to receive him at court with greatest honors.

Don Gomez: What a mistake! Her Majesty is too ready to believe whatever she is told.

Secretary: But think of the Indians whom he has brought back with him! We never saw men like them before.

Don Gomez: I am a matter-of-fact man. Mark my words; it will turn out a trick. We shall find that Columbus sailed south instead of west and didn't discover anything.

Secretary: The sailors all say they steered west.

Don Gomez: A trick! A trick! Would you have me believe that an unknown coast has been reached by sailing west? Impossible! You know that the earth can't be round, for men would be standing on their heads down on the other sides. Oh no! I'm a plain matter-of-fact man, sir. Call my carriage. I must go to the palace and show the king that Columbus is all wrong.

Columbus at the Court of Spain

Alexander Vinent

Isabella, Queen of Spain.
Don Gomez, adviser to the king and queen.
Columbus, a sea captain from Italy.

TIME: April, 1492.
PLACE: A room in the palace.

Columbus has been telling the queen of his belief that the earth is round and that he can reach India by sailing west. He has asked for help so that he can make the voyage to prove that he is right.

Queen: Don Gomez, you have heard what this stranger has said. Do you think we ought to help him?

Don Gomez: Indeed, your Majesty, his plan is all a wild dream. I am a plain matter-of-fact man and do not see such visions.

Queen: But Columbus has given us good reasons for his beliefs and plans.

Don Gomez: You surely know that the earth is flat. Even if it were round, as he thinks, how could he possibly return if he once went down the sides of the earth? Wouldn't he have to come up hill all the way? A ship could never do that! Oh no, he will only fall over the edge if he goes too far!

Columbus: You know that men have sailed far out of sight upon the ocean and have come safely back. I, too, shall be able to bring my ship home.

Don Gomez: Your Majesty, this man would have us believe that people are living on the other side of the earth. Then they must be walking with their heads down, like flies on the ceiling. And I suppose he would have us believe that there the trees grow with their branches downward, and it rains and snows upwards. No, no! I am a plain matter-of-fact man, I cannot believe that.

Columbus: But, your Majesty, there are things about the earth that men have not yet learned. I can explain to you why the people on the opposite side of the earth walk just as we do.

Don Gomez: Oh, very well! Very well! But I must believe what I can see. I know that I am not walking with my head downwards. And yet any one living down there, as you say, with his feet opposite to mine, must be upside down.

Queen: Then you think that we should listen no longer to the words of Columbus?

Don Gomez: It is all folly, I am sure of it. Has your Majesty ever seen any person from this strange land that he wishes to find?

Queen: Don Gomez, have you ever seen any one from the unknown land to which we go after death?

Don Gomez: Certainly not; but I have faith that we shall go there.

Queen: Columbus, too, has faith. It is by faith that he looks across the vast ocean to the distant land.

Columbus: Your Majesty is right. But I have reasons, too, strong reasons for the faith that is in me. I know that I can sail far to the west and find the new way to India.

Don Gomez: Oh yes, you can sail away, and we shall never hear of you again. You must give us facts, solid facts, before we plain matter-of-fact people will risk any money on your plans. Give no more heed to him, your Majesty. Why, even the boys on the street point to their foreheads as he passes.

Queen: Do you think the jeering of boys at what they do not understand can influence Isabella? I have faith in all that is spoken by this earnest man. I am ready to test his great and glorious plan, even though you call it folly.

Don Gomez: Your Majesty will pardon me if I remind you of what the king himself has said. He has no funds to help Columbus.

Queen: Then I will fit out the ships for him. I have jewels of great value, which I will use to raise the money. It shall be done without a moment's delay.

Columbus: Your Majesty shall never regret this noble decision. I shall return. Be sure, your Majesty, that I shall return and lay at your feet such a jewel as never yet was worn by any queen. I have faith that I shall succeed and that men shall forever bless you for your service to-day.

Quotations for Columbus Day

Columbus's discovery of the New World was the effect of an active genius, acting upon a regular plan, executed with no less courage than perseverance.— *Robertson.*

Little wonder that the whole world takes from the life of Columbus one of its best-beloved illustrations of the absolute power of faith. To a faithless world he made a proposal, and the world did not hear it. To that faithless world he made it again and again, and at last roused the world to ridicule it and to contradict it. To the same faithless world he still made it year after year; and at last the world said that, when it was ready, it would try if he were right; to which his only reply is that he is ready now, that the world must send him now on the expedition which shall show whether he is right or wrong. The world, tired of his importunity, consents, unwillingly enough, that he shall try the experiment. He tries it; he succeeds; and the world turns round and welcomes him with a welcome which it cannot give to a conqueror. In a moment the grandeur of his plans is admitted, their success is acknowledged, and his place is fixed as one of the great men of history.— *Edward Everett Hale.*

With all the visionary fervor of his imagination, its fondest dreams fell short of the reality. He died in ignorance of the real grandeur of his discovery. Until his last breath he entertained the idea that he had merely opened a new way to the old resorts of opulent commerce, and had discovered some of the wild regions of the East. What visions of glory would have broken upon his mind, could he have known that he had indeed discovered a new continent, equal to the old world in magnitude, and separated by two vast oceans, from all the earth hitherto known by civilized man! How would his magnanimous spirit have been consoled amid the afflictions of age and the cares of penury, the neglect of a fickle public and the injustices of an ungrateful king, could he have anticipated the splendid empires which would arise in the beautiful world he had discovered; and the nations, and tongues, and languages, which were to fill its land with his renown, and to revere and bless his name to the latest posterity.— *Washington Irving.*

One storm-trained seaman listened to the word;
What no man saw he saw, and heard what no man heard.
  For answer he compelled the sea
    To eager man to tell
    The secret she had kept so well;
  Left blood and woe and tyranny behind,
  Sailing still west the land newborn to find,
  For all mankind the unstained page unfurled
Where God might write anew the story of the world.
               — *Edward Everett Hale.*

He had fully established the truth of his long-contested theory, in the face of argument, sophistry, sneer, skepticism, and contempt. He had achieved this, not by chance, but by calculation, supported through the most adverse circumstances by consummate conduct.— *William H. Prescott.*

In the fulness of time Columbus came. New forces had come to light of late,— the mariner's compass, gunpowder, printing, the spur of intellectual awakening. It was for Columbus, when the right hour struck, forced and propelled by this fresh life, to reveal the land where these new principles were to be brought, and where the awaited trial of the new civilization was to be made.— *Francis Bellamy.*

Behold the crowning gift to America, from Columbus, whose caravels plowed ocean's uncertain billows in search of a great land, and from the all-ruling Providence, whose wisdom and mercy inspired and guided the immortal Genoese Mariner — the United States of America.— *Archbishop John Ireland.*

Neither realism nor romance furnishes a more striking and picturesque figure than that of Christopher Columbus. The mystery about his origin heightens the charm of his story. That he came from among the toilers of his time is in harmony with the struggles of our period. The perils of the sea in his youth upon the rich argosies of Genoa, or in the service of the licensed rovers who made them their prey, had developed a skillful navigator and intrepid mariner. To secure the means to test the truth of his speculations this poor and unknown dreamer must win the support of kings and overcome the hostility of the Church. He never doubted his ability to do both.— *Chauncey M. Depew.*

All hail, Columbus, discoverer, dreamer, hero, and apostle! We here, of every race and country, recognize the horizon which bounded his vision and the infinite scope of his genius. The voice of gratitude and praise for all the blessings which have been showered upon mankind by adventure is limited to no language, but is uttered in every tongue. Neither marble nor brass can fitly form his statue. Continents are his monument, and unnumbered millions, past, present, and to come, who enjoy in their liberties and their happiness the fruits of his faith, will reverently guard and preserve, from century to century, his name and fame.— *Chauncey M. Depew.*

> He failed fulfillment of the task he planned
> And drooped a weary head on empty hand,
> Unconscious of the vaster deed he'd done;
> But royal legacy to Ferdinand
> He left — a key to doorways gilt with sun —
> And proudest title of " World-father " won!
> — *George W. W. Houghton.*

The Roosevelt Creed

I believe in honesty, sincerity, and the square deal; in making up one's mind what to do — and doing it.

I believe in fearing God and taking one's own part.

I believe in hitting the line hard when you are right.

I believe in hard work and honest sport.

I believe in a sane mind in a sane body.

I believe we have room for but one soul loyalty, and that in loyalty to the American people.

ROOSEVELT DAY

October 27

The anniversary of the birth of Theodore Roosevelt has not been made a legal holiday in any state. However, since his death on January 6, 1919, there has been considerable agitation for some legal recognition of his birth. He was born in New York City on October 27, 1858. He has always been a popular favorite with school children because of his love for all things connected with nature, hunting and exploring.

Theodore Roosevelt

Samuel Valentine Cole

HALF-MAST the flag, and let the bell be tolled:
   A tower of strength he was, whose presence drew
The people around him, and to-day is rolled
   A wave of unaccustomed sorrow through
The land he loved; whatever now be said,
The latest great American is dead.

How quick he slipped from us — this man of might,
   Heroic courage, life-abounding ways!
When God's great angel in the silent night
   Brought, though invisible to others' gaze,
Some whispered message, he obediently heard,
Left all, and followed him without a word.

We loved this man who loved not fame, or wealth,
   But service, first; not perfect, or divine,
But humanlike, and full of moral health,
   And prompt to look beyond the outward sign
Of race, or creed, or party, find the plan
Of God himself, and recognize the man.

How true his vision was! And how his voice
   Seemed as a breeze does on a sultry day!
Long years ago he made life's master-choice,
   Like a brave knight of conscience, and alway
Dared wield the club of language clear and strong
To shield the right and batter down the wrong.

He stood for honest purposes: unroll
   The record of his years, you seek in vain
For life's disfigurements — there lies the scroll,
   No blots upon it, nothing to explain;
But what is worthy and to all men's sight
As open as a landscape to the light.

Farewell, great Soul! Thou surely wilt fare well
   On that mysterious and adventurous way
Which thou hast gone; in those realms also dwell
   Truth, right, and honor, and God's love bears sway
To these, as in our bounds of time and place,
Thou art no stranger; they will know thy face.

There Washington and Lincoln stretch to thee
   The hand of welcome; they are working still
For some high end as once for liberty;
   Thou art at one with them in aim and will,
The peer of them in doing well thy part,
And their companion in the Nation's heart.

So lived this man, and died, and lives again —
   A white dynamic memory in the land.
Oh, what a heritage, my countrymen!
   He'll plead forever now, with voice and hand,
Our righteous causes, and his power will grow.
Cease tolling, bell, and let the bugles blow!

Theodore Roosevelt — Pilot and Prophet!

Charles Hanson Towne

I

On what divine adventure has he gone?
Beyond what peaks of dawn
Is he now faring? On what errand blest
Has his impulsive heart now turned? No rest
Could be the portion of his tireless soul.
He seeks some frenzied goal
Where he can labor on till Time is not,
And earth is nothing but a thing forgot.

II

Pilot and Prophet! as the years increase
The sorrow of your passing will not cease.
We love to think of you still moving on
From sun to blazing sun,
From planet to far planet, to some height
Of clear perfection in the Infinite,
Where with the wise Immortals you can find
The Peace you fought for with your heart and mind.
Yet from that bourne where you are journeying
Sometimes we think we hear you whispering,
" I went away, O world, so false and true,
I went away — with still so much to do! "

Roosevelt

T. E. Thomas

'Twas not in him to deal with cringing touch
Or remonstrate with fawning plaint —
His honest, virile heart was never faint.
Nor had he faith in those whose acts were such
That led to doubt their aim in any fight.
To him all things were either wrong or right;
No compromise was his, with purpose whole,
He favored or opposed with all his soul.

No foeman's steel brought terror to his eyes;
No sycophancy could he endure,
Nor aught that was not plain and pure.
His friendship was no traitors' paradise;
He measured men and deeds with common sense,
And gave to each in turn fair recompense
As they deserved, of either blame or praise,
For his were always just, not devious ways.

A master mind was his, both brilliant and profound,
Gifted with a reasoning rare;
Boldly 'twas his to do and dare,
With precept manly and with judgment sound.
No sophist's plea nor sham could bar his way;
Each act with him must bear the open light of day;
No half-way measure sought, could satisfy
Or meet his questioning of How or Why.

He served his time, his people, and his land,
And as he sowed, so did he reap.

The silent summons found him in his sleep.
Peaceful in death, in resignation grand,
His glorious soul has through the portal flown
To meet the only master it had ever known.
From earth's great trials triumphantly it passed,
Fighting at Armageddon to the last.

Roosevelt

Robert H. Davis

HE came out the void
Buoyed upon the surging tides.
He braved the West,
Defied the wide frontiers;
He trekked the continents
And enthroned his name
Among the white, the black, the brown, the yellow men.
He trod the frond,
Fording the darkened streams
That glide through jungles
To the tropic sea.
He spanned the globe,
He swept the skies,
And moved beneath the eaters of the deep.
He entered all the portals of the world,
A vibrant, thrilled, exhaustless, restless soul;
Riding at last the very stars —
Asleep.

Roosevelt

Peter Fandel

COLUMBIA,
If aught but loss of honor
Or decay of principle
May set the well springs of thy tears aflow,
The occasion now is thine.
For he, thy champion supreme,
Who took his heartbeats from thine own,
Was snatched from thee all unforewarned
And left thee desolate and bereft.
Yes, he thy son, who ever stood by thee
And all his soul in loving beyance held
Unto thy intimate counsel and demand,
In the very hour of thy sorest need
Has fallen a prey to the grim reaper — Death.
How proud he was! how faithful, and how strong!
He, with the indomitable courage of a lion,
Stood constant guard beside thee and
With jealous eye scanned every act
That dared assail thy honor or besmirch.
Strong sinewed, both of mind and limb,
He feared no ill-designing foe,
Nor the enmity of those who tried
To shield corruptive will or suffered wrong
Behind the barriers of thy glorious aegis,
He was a man of men —
One who summed our divergent strength
And roused our conscience from submissive sloth
Against the infesting evils of the day.
He rested not nor slumbered,
But breathed his fiery spirit in the land

Till it became therewith aflame
And scourged the felonous sin thereof.
And if from labors in the vicious pit
He came not forth entirely unscathed,
Or, in devotion to the cause,
Perchance sometimes o'erreached himself,
The blame should not be counted his;
For noble souls to virtues may transmute
Oft traits of human frailty
And thus be more deserving still.
But, when, by the receding past,
He in perspective true shall once be brought
And loom forth free from personal animosities
And the contrarieties of feeling
And strange antagonisms of mind
That dis-esteem in shallow mortals breed,
He shall appear in true proportions —
Proportions that shall measure well
With those of our heroic dead
Who live on still in our institutions
And are their glory and enduring worth.

With the Tide

Edith Wharton

SOMEWHERE I read, in an old book whose name
Is gone from me, I read that when the days
Of a man are counted, and his business done,
There comes up the shore at evening, with the tide,
To the place where he sits, a boat —
And in the boat, from the place where he sees,
Dim in the dusk, dim and yet so familiar,
The faces of his friends long dead; and knows

They come for him, brought in upon the tide,
To take him where men go at set of day.
Then rising, with his hands in theirs, he goes
Between them his last steps, that are the first
Of the new life — and with the ebb they pass,
Their shaken sail grown small upon the moon.

Often I thought of this, and pictured me
How many a man who lives with throngs about him,
Yet straining through the twilight for that boat
Shall scarce make out one figure in the stern,
And that so faint its features shall perplex him
With doubtful memories — and his heart hang back.
But others, rising as they see the sail
Increase upon the sunset, hasten down,
Hands out and eyes elated; for they see
Head over head, crowding from bow to stern,
Re-peeping their long loneliness with smiles,
The faces of their friends; and such go forth
Content upon the ebb tide, with safe hearts.

But never
To worker summoned when his day was done
Did mounting tide bring in such freight of friends,
As stole to you up the white wintry shingle
That night while they watched you though you slept,
Softly they came, and beached the boat, and gathered
In the still cove under the icy stars,
Your last-born, and the dear loves of your heart,
And all men that have loved right more than ease,
And honor above honors; all who gave
Free-handed of their best for other men,
And thought their giving taking; they who knew
Man's natural state is effort, up and up —

All these were there, so great a company
Perchance you marveled, wondering what great ship
Had brought that throng unnumbered to the cove
Where the boys used to beach their light canoe
After old happy picnics —

But these, your friends and children, to whose hands
Committed, in the silent night you rose
And took your last faint steps —
These led you down, O great American,
Down to the Winter night and the white beach,
And there you saw that the huge hull that waited
Was not as are the boats of the other dead,
Frail craft for a brief passage; no, for this
Was first of a long line of towering transports,
Storm-worn and ocean-weary every one,
The ships you launched, the ships you manned, the ships
That now, returning from their sacred quest
With the thrice-sacred burden of their dead,
Lay waiting there to take you forth with them,
Out with the ebb tide, on some farther quest.

Close up the Ranks

Edward S. Van Zile

I

GENTLY Death came to him and bent to him asleep;
His spirit passed, and lo, his lovers weep,
But not for him, for him the unafraid —
In tears, we ask, " Who'll lead the great crusade?

II

" Who'll hearten us to carry on the war
For those ideals our fathers battled for;
To give our hearts to one dear flag alone,
The flag beloved whose splendid soul has flown?"

III

With his last breath he gave a clarion cry:
" They only serve who do not fear to die;
He only lives who's worthy of our dead!
Beware the peril of the seed that's spread.

IV

" By them who'll reap a harvest of despair,
By them whose dreams unstable are as air;
By them who see the rainbow in the sky,
But not the storm that threatens by and by."

V

Our leader rests, his voice forever still,
But let us vow to do our leader's will!
Close up the ranks!   Our Captain is not dead!
His soul shall live, and by his soul we're led;

VI

Led forward fighting for the real, the true,
Not turned aside by what the dreamers do.
If he could speak he would not have us weep,
But souls awake whose Captain lies asleep.

American Ideals

Theodore Roosevelt

EVERY great nation owes to the men whose lives have formed part of its greatness not merely the material effect of what they did, not merely the laws they placed upon the statute books or the victories they won over armed foes, but also the immense but indefinable moral influence produced by their deeds and words themselves upon the national character.

It would be difficult to exaggerate the material effects of the careers of Washington and of Lincoln upon the United States. Without Washington we should probably never have won our independence of the British crown, and we should almost certainly have failed to become a great nation, remaining instead a cluster of jangling little communities, drifting toward the type of government prevalent in Spanish America. Without Lincoln we might perhaps have failed to keep the political unity we had won; and even if, as is possible, we had kept it, both the struggle by which it was kept and the results of this struggle would have been so different that the effect upon our national history could not have failed to be profound.

Yet the nation's debt to these men is not confined to what it owes them for its material well-being, incalculable though this debt is. Beyond the fact that we are an independent and united people, with half a continent as our heritage, lies the fact that every American is richer by the heritage of the noble deeds and noble words of Washington and of Lincoln.

Sayings of Theodore Roosevelt

A man who is good enough to shed his blood for the country is good enough to be given a square deal afterwards. — *From the " Life of Benton."*

The man who becomes Europeanized, who loses his power of doing good work on this side of the water and who loses his love for his native land is not a traitor, but he is a silly and undesirable citizen.— *From " American Ideals."*

We do not wish, in politics, in literature, or in art, to develop that unwholesome parochial spirit, that over-exaltation of the little community at the expense of the great nation, which produces what has been described as the patriotism of the village, the patriotism of the belfry. . . . The patriotism of the village or the belfry is bad, but the lack of all patriotism is even worse.— *From " American Ideals."*

I wish to preach, not the doctrine of ignoble ease, but the doctrine of the strenuous life, the life of toil and effort, of labor and strife; to preach that highest form of success which comes, not to the man who desires mere easy peace, but to the man who does not shrink from danger, from hardship, or from bitter toil, and who out of these wins the splendid ultimate triumph.— *From " The Strenuous Life."*

There is no moral difference between gambling at cards or in lotteries or on the race track and gambling in the stock market. One method is just as pernicious to the body politic as the other kind, and in degree the evil worked is far greater.— *From a Special Message.*

One of the prime dangers of civilization has always been its tendency to cause the loss of the virile fighting qualities, of the fighting edge. When men get too comfortable and lead too luxurious lives, there is always danger lest the softness eat like an acid into their manliness of fibre. The barbarian, because of the very condition of his life, is forced to keep and develop certain hardy qualities which the man of civilization tends to lose, whether he be clerk, factory hand, merchant, or even a certain type of farmer.— *From an Address at the University of Berlin.*

In our complex industrial civilization of to-day the peace of righteousness and justice, the only kind of peace worth having, is at least as necessary in the industrial world as it is among nations.   There is at least as much need to curb the cruel greed and arrogance of part of the world of capital, to curb the cruel greed and violence of part of the world of labor, as to check a cruel and unhealthy militarism in international relationships.— *From an Address at the University of Berlin.*

So long as I have any influence left I shall protest against arbitration between this and any other country which will not keep its agreements.   Arbitration is all well enough under favorable conditions, but not otherwise.   It isn't right to arbitrate with a country when you know that that country will not keep an agreement if it comes to a pinch.

If you think that the people of the United States want universal peace arbitration I suggest that you go to California and investigate conditions.   I have no use for liars, national, international, or those found in private life.— *From a Speech at Arlington Cemetery.*

In the last twenty years an increasing percentage of our people have come to depend on industry for their livelihood, so that to-day the wage workers in industry rank in importance side by side with the tiller of the soil.   As a people we cannot afford to let any group of citizens, any individual citizens, live or labor under conditions which are injurious to the common welfare.   Industry, therefore, must submit to such public regulation as will make it a means of life and health, not of death or inefficiency.   We must protect the crushable elements at the base of our present industrial structure.— *From a Speech at Chicago.*

It seems to me that we should realize with the keenest gratitude how much we owe to the fact that by steady application of the Monroe Doctrine this country has succeeded in preventing the colonization of this continent by the great military Old World powers. If it had not been for the existence of that doctrine, and its support by this Government under Presidents of all shades of political belief, the great military nations of the Old World would unquestionably long ere this have possessed masses of territory in the western hemisphere. In such case nothing under heaven could have prevented our being involved in European struggles like the present. We would also in such case be under the crushing burden of immense armaments in time of peace, a burden the bearing of which has grown more enormous year by year in Europe. Well meaning and amiable but short-sighted persons have from time to time protested against the Monroe Doctrine and said it was outworn. I wish these good persons would seriously consider the present contest and realize that if it had not been for the Monroe Doctrine in the past, and if the Monroe Doctrine were at this moment abandoned, the United States would, in all probability, have been drawn into the present dreadful struggle.— *From a Speech at Hartford, Conn.*

Professional pacifists, the peace-at-any-price, non-resistance, universal arbitration people are seeking to Chinafy this country.— *From a Speech at San Francisco.*

America is not to be made a polyglot boarding house for money hunters of twenty different nationalities who have changed their former country for this country only as farmyard beasts change one feeding trough for another. America is a nation. No man has any right to come here and no man should be permitted to stay here unless he becomes an American and nothing else. Be loyal to the principles established by Washington and his fellows in 1776 and perpetuated by Lincoln and his fellows in 1861 and 1865. We must have in this country only one flag, and that flag the

American flag; only one language, the English language, the language of the Declaration of Independence, Washington's Farewell Address, Lincoln's Gettysburg speech and the second inaugural; and but one loyalty, that to the United States.— *From a Speech to Munition Workers, at Bridgeport, Conn.*

You stand up when "The Star Spangled Banner" is sung, not because of men who previously sang it, but because of the men who stood the bombardment through the night — for the men who stood up to the killing and did the killing when the need came. That is why you are proud to be Americans now. Talking amounts to less than nothing, save just to the degree in which it is turned into action, and in this country of ours the man who is not only ready to fight for it, but to fit himself to fight for it, the man who has not raised himself to be a soldier, and the woman who has not raised her boy to be a soldier for the right — neither one of them is entitled to citizenship in the Republic. Universal suffrage, to justify itself, must be based on universal service. It is only you and your kind who have the absolutely clear title to the management of this Republic.— *From a Speech to the Soldiers at Camp Upton.*

As regards Americanism, we must insist that there be in this country but one nationality, the American nationality. There must be no perpetuation in this country of separate national groups, with their separate languages and special loyalties to alien overseas flags. There can be no fifty-fifty Americanism in this country. There is room here for only 100 per cent. Americanism, only for those who are Americans and nothing else. We must have loyalty to only one flag, the American flag; and it is disloyal to the American flag to try to be loyal to any other, whether that other is a foreign flag or the black and red flag which symbolize either anarchy or else treacherous hostility to a war for which the nation stands.— *From a Speech at a Republican Convention at Saratoga.*

Tributes to Theodore Roosevelt

The appeal of Mr. Roosevelt to the American people for justice, equal rights, and a fair opportunity for all gives symmetry and cohesion to his varied administrations as Civil Service Commissioner, Police Commissioner, Assistant Secretary of the Navy, Lieutenant-Colonel in the Army, Governor of New York, and President of the United States. It made him as bitter enemies in influential quarters as any man in American politics has ever known; but it also made him the most widely admired and best-beloved American of his time.

And it did more. It went far toward converting American politics from a trade to a profession; it inspired his colleagues and his party associates; it summoned into political activity followers in both parties and in all sections of the country. Men had thought of politics as a traffic which no man can enter into without dishonor. His life proved to them that the highest success is possible to honor, courage, and purity if mated to ability. It raised the ideals and the standards of public life for the entire American people. Its influence in creating the genuine and self-sacrificing patriotism which called the Nation into this world war with a voice which love of ease and dread of war could not resist cannot be estimated. And it has done more than any other one influence, if not more than all other influences combined, to inspire the citizens of this country with a real faith in the intelligence and virtue of their fellow-men, and so in the practicability of that self-government which is the foundation of a true democracy because of a true brotherhood of man.— *Lyman Abbott*.

Theodore Roosevelt's death removes 'the one powerful personal influence in American politics. His distinguishing quality among the Americans of his own generation was an abounding energy which required for its satisfaction both great variety and exuberant vigor of expression. He was almost alone among his contemporaries in the extraordinary diversity of his interests. He was at once a man of letters, an insatiable reader, a brilliant talker, a naturalist, a sportsman and a political leader. He found time to pursue all these activities with so much success that they effectively contributed to the vivid impression made by his personality. But exceptional as was the variety of his activities, the sheer vigor which he imparted to them was still more exceptional.

Whatever he did, and no matter whether he was the head of the Government or the head of the opposition, he always set the pace. It was his joy and his pride to work harder, to play harder, to fight harder than any associate or any competitor. In fact, his energy was so strenuous that it seemed to him wasted unless it expended itself in overcoming a stiff resistance. Only in combat did he reach the summit of his personal expression. When asked before an election to express some opinion as to its probable results, he always answered: " I am a warrior and not a prophet." He was a warrior on behalf of what he believed to be and usually were morally decisive causes. The most poignant tragedy of his life was that he was unable to fight sword in hand in the war which raised one of the clearest and greatest moral issues in history.

It was as a warrior on behalf of moral causes that he made his most substantial contribution to American history. Associated from the beginning with the reforming activities of his own contemporaries, he was the first of our political leaders who dared to remain a reformer after he reached the White House. In fact, he nationalized the American reform movement and by nationalizing transfigured it. He divined that American national fulfilment had come to depend not on the preservation of institutions but on the cure of abuses, not on conservation but on progress.— *New Republic.*

His leadership, although not always followed by the majority of his countrymen, was universally regarded as a healthful and invigorating influence in the national existence, and there is absolutely no one remaining in public life who can take the place he occupied in the hearts of the people.

No matter what Colonel Roosevelt said or did in his impetuous, outspoken, belligerent way, and however his expressed opinions might fail of getting acceptance, there was that quality in his character which made him strong to the affections of his fellow-citizens, and to the end he held a unique and wholly exceptional position in this respect. His distinguished and remarkable career, his manliness, his force and courage, the great versatility of his accomplishments, his quick, eager, restless temperament, his lust for achievements and the ability which he displayed in all that he undertook, these and the manifold traits which were exhibited in his complex nature, all served to make him a popular hero, of whom the American people were both fond and proud, however they might differ from him in certain of his expressed convictions.— *Bellman — Minneapolis.*

To the Giver of all blessings
Let our voices rise in praise
For the joys and countless mercies
He hath sent to crown our days;
For the homes of peace and plenty,
And a land so fair and wide,
For the labor at the noonday,
And the rest at eventide.

— William G. Park.

THANKSGIVING DAY

November —

Thanksgiving Day originated when Governor Bradford of the little colony of Pilgrims, after the first gathering of the harvest in the New World, sent four men out to shoot wild fowl that the infant colony "might after a more special manner rejoice together." For many years the autumnal feast of Thanksgiving was merely an occasional festival. It was not until the Civil War had brought the people to a new feeling of national unity that the day has been recognized generally. Since 1863 the President of the United States has annually issued a Thanksgiving proclamation calling on the people to observe the last Thursday in November to give thanks for the blessings they have received during the preceding year.

Let Us Give Thanks

Marianne Farningham

For the discipline of sorrow,
　For the angel of distress,
For the unseen hands that draw us
　Into greater blessedness;
For the lips that close in silence
　For the strong hands clasped in prayer,
For the strength of heart that suffers,
　But sinks not in despair;
For the penitence and patience
　That are meek beneath the rod,
And for hope's glad resurrection,
　We give Thee thanks, O God.

For the hope that right shall triumph,
　For the lifting of the race,
For the victories of justice,
　For a coming day of grace,
For the lessons taught by failure,
　Learnt in humbleness and pain,
For the call to lofty duties
　That will come to us again,
For the hope that those who trust in God
　Shall not be put to shame,
For the faith that lives in all the world,
　O God! we praise Thy name.

We Thank Thee

Mattie M. Renwick

For flowers so beautiful and sweet,
For friends and clothes and food to eat,
For precious hours, for work and play,
We thank Thee this Thanksgiving Day.

For father's care and mother's love,
For the blue sky and clouds above,
For springtime and autumn gay
We thank Thee this Thanksgiving Day!

For all Thy gifts so good and fair,
Bestowed so freely everywhere,
Give us grateful hearts we pray,
To thank Thee this Thanksgiving Day.

Thanksgiving

Florence Earle Coates

Thou that dost save through pain,
 And dost, afflicting, bless,
We offer Thee from prostrate hearts
 The Greater Thankfulness!

Lord, Thou hast humbled pride —
 Hast shown the world at length
What ruthlessness may dwell with Power,
 What bankruptcy with Strength;

And teaching us the scorn
    Of trifles that beguile,
Hast given us, dear God, to live
    When life is most worth while!

We thank Thee for the dream
    That heroes dreamed of yore,
For the desire of good, the will
    Earth's freedom to restore;

Spoiled children of the Past,
    To-day, more nobly blest,
We thank Thee Who hast awakened us,
    And asked of us our best!

God of the young and brave
    Who nothing know of fear,
Who hold the things that life outlast
    Than life itself more dear,

We thank Thee that our souls
    Are strong as theirs to give —
All, all we cherish most on earth,
    That Liberty may live!

That we, O Good supreme!
    Still through our tears can see
On the brow of Death an aureole
    Of Immortality!

Giving Thanks

Anonymous

For the hay and the corn and the wheat that is reaped,
For the labor well done, and the barns that are heaped,
For the sun and the dew and the sweet honeycomb,
For the rose and the song, and the harvest brought
    home —
    Thanksgiving! Thanksgiving!

For the trade and the skill and the wealth in our land,
For the cunning and strength of the workingman's hand,
For the good that our artists and poets have taught,
For the friendship that hope and affection have brought —
    Thanksgiving! Thanksgiving!

For the homes that with purest affection are blest,
For the season of plenty and well deserved rest,
For our country extending from sea unto sea,
The land that is known as the " Land of the Free "—
    Thanksgiving! Thanksgiving!

Thanksgiving for Thanksgiving

Amos R. Wells

I thank Thee, Father, once again
    For many blessings gladly known,
And many more beyond my ken
    That Thou dost see and Thou alone;
But most of all my heart I raise
To praise Thee for the power to praise.

Thy bounty, it is wondrous kind;
　　But oh, the smiling of Thy face!
My life is all in love designed,
　　But Thou Thyself are grace of grace,—
Thyself, oh, infinitely more
Than all Thy bounty's golden store.

That I can feel Thy Fatherhood,
　　That I can press my hand in Thine,
That I can know that Thou art good,
　　And all Thy power is love divine,—
This knowledge every bliss outranks;
I thank Thee for the gift of thanks.

Every Day Thanksgiving Day

Harriet Prescott Spofford

SWEET it is to see the sun
　　Shining on Thanksgiving Day,
Sweet it is to see the snow
　　Fall as if it came to stay;
Sweet is everything that comes,
　　For all makes cheer, Thanksgiving Day.

Fine is the pantry's goodly store,
　　And fine the heaping dish and tray;
Fine the church-bells ringing; fine
　　All the dinners' great array,
Things we'd hardly dare to touch,
　　Were it not Thanksgiving Day.

Dear the people coming home,
　　Dear glad faces long away,

Dear the merry cries, and dear
    All the gay and happy play.
Dear the thanks, too, that we give
    For all of this Thanksgiving Day.

But sweeter, finer, dearer far
    It well might be if on our way,
With love for all, with thanks to Heaven,
    We did not wait for time's delay,
But with remembered blessings then
    Made every day Thanksgiving Day!

A Thanksgiving

Carolyn Wells

DEEPEST thanksgiving I do give,
Because I didn't chance to live
In what they call the " good old days "
Of homely fare and simple ways.

I like the days that we have now,
Instead of broom and churn and plow;
I like to have a bed with springs,
And telephones and vacuum things.

Those " good old times," so praised in song!
How did the women get along?
No bridge or suffrage or bead bags,
No motor-cars or gladsome rags!

I'm very glad " old-fashioned cheer "
Will not be offered me this year;
No squash or pumpkin pie for me —
I much prefer patisserie.

I can't see how they lived at all
Without a cab or music-hall;
Oh, earnestly I do thanks give
That our times are not primitive!

A Harvest Song

Edwin Markham

THE gray hulk of the granary uplooms against the sky;
The harvest moon has dwindled — they have housed the
　　corn and rye;
And now the idle reapers lounge against the bolted doors:
Without are hungry harvesters, within enchanted stores.

Lo, they had bread while they were out a-toiling in the
　　sun:
Now, they are strolling beggars, for the harvest work
　　is done.
They are the gods of husbandry: they gather in the
　　sheaves,
But when the autumn strips the wood, they're drifting
　　with the leaves.

They plow and sow and gather in the glory of the corn;
They know the noon, they know the pitiless rains before
　　the morn;
They know the sweep of furrowed fields that darkened in
　　the gloom —
A little while their hope on earth, then evermore their
　　tomb.

Thanksgiving

Odell Shepard

For raiment and for daily bread,
    For shelter from the rain and shine,
For length of days and hardihead,
    Small gratitude is mine.

These are the laborer's due hire,
    Tho hard it be to solve the doubt
How I have merited the fire
    My brother goes without.

But for the mission of my feet,
    The labor of my heart and hand,
The service difficult and sweet
    And all my own, I stand

Most deeply thankful, and for art
    That nerves my strength and fires my brain,
For song, that ever calls my heart
    Back to its dreams again.

For the assurance that my toil
    Is furthering some mighty end
Beyond the present strife and moil,
    Toward which the ages trend.

For labor, wageless tho it be,
    For what I give, not what I take,
For battle, not for victory,
    My prayer of thanks I make.

Thanksgiving Day

J. J. Montague

WITH steadfast and unwavering faith, with hard and
patient toil,
The Pilgrims wrung their harvest from a strange and
sterile soil.
And when the leaves turned red and gold beneath the
autumn sun,
They knelt beside the scanty sheaves their laboring hands
had won,
And each grave elder, in his turn, with bowed and reverent head,
Gave thanks to bounteous Heaven for the miracle of
bread.

And so was born Thanksgiving Day. That little daunt-
less band,
Beset by deadly perils in a wild and alien land,
With hearts that held no fear of death, with stern, un-
bending wills,
And faith as firmly founded as the grim New England
hills,
Though pitiful the yield that sprang from that unfruit-
ful sod,
Remembered, in their harvest time, the goodly grace of
God.

In miles of bursting granaries our golden grain is stored,
And countless families are drawn round many a groan-
ing board.
The wilderness the Pilgrims won a favoring Heaven has
blessed

With all the vast and wondrous yield of Mother Nature's
    breast.
And while across the Eastern sea there shrieks the battle
    call,
To-day to us is given Peace, most priceless gift of all.

God grant us grace to look on this, our glorious native
    land,
As but another princely gift from His almighty hand.
May we prove worthy of His trust and keep its every
    shore
Protected from the murderous hordes that bear the torch
    of war,
And be the future bright or dark, God grant we never
    may
Forget the reverent spirit of that first Thanksgiving Day!

Thanksgiving Night

Wilbur D. Nesbit

LAST night I got to thinking, when I couldn't go to sleep,
Of the way Thanksgiving served me in the days when joy
    was cheap —
Of how we'd have a turkey, and of how I'd beg a taste
Whenever they would open up the oven door to " baste "
The bulging breast, and how then from the oven came a
    drift
Of tantalizing odor, such as only boys have sniffed.

I got to thinking of it — for I couldn't go to sleep —
Of mince pies in the pantry, where I'd sidle in and peep,
And jelly and plum butter, and the peach preserves and
    cake —

And then I got to thinking of how fine 'twould be to take
A trip back to the old days, when the dancing candle
light
Played pranks with all the shadows on the wall, Thanksgiving night.

The boys I used to play with! I could shut my eyes
and see
The whole troop of them waiting and a-waving hands
to me;
All freckled, ragged-trousered, with their scarfs and mit-
tens, too,
They made a splendid picture — but the picture wasn't
true;
For they've grown up, as I have, and strange paths have
lured our feet —
The paths that find To-morrow, and that never, never
meet.

I wondered if they also were not lying half awake
And thinking of the turkey, and the jelly, and the cake;
And if they had their fancies of the lazy little street
That leads beneath the maples where the topmost
branches meet —
And suddenly I heard them — heard the murmurs low
and clear,
That told me they were with me, and were very, very
near.

Thanksgiving

Amelia E. Barr

FIRST PUPIL:

" Have you cut the wheat in the blowing fields,
  The barley, the oats, and the nodding rye,
The golden corn and the pearly rice?
  For the winter days draw nigh."

SECOND PUPIL:

" We have reaped them all from shore to shore,
And the grain is safe on the threshing floor."

THIRD PUPIL:

" Have you gathered the berries from the vine,
  And the fruit from the orchard trees?
The dew and the scent from the roses and thyme,
  In the hive of the honey bees? "

FOURTH PUPIL:

" The peach and the plum and the apple are ours,
And the honey-comb from the scented flowers."

FIFTH PUPIL:

" The wealth of the snowy cotton field
  And the gift of the sugar cane,
The savory herb and the nourishing root —
  There has been nothing given in vain."

SIXTH PUPIL:

" We have gathered the harvest from shore to shore,
And the measure is full and brimming o'er."

ALL:
　　Then lift up the head with a song!
　　　　And lift up the hand with a gift!
　　To the ancient Giver of all
　　　　The spirit in gratitude lift!
　　For the joy and the promise of spring,
　　　　For the hay and the clover sweet,
　　The barley, the rye and the oats,
　　　　The rice and the corn and the wheat,
　　The cotton and sugar and fruit,
　　　　The flowers and the fine honey-comb,
　　The country so fair and so free,
　　　　The blessings and glory of home.

Thanksgiving Day

Lydia Maria Child

OVER the river and through the wood,
　　To grandfather's house we'll go;
　　　　The horse knows the way
　　　　To carry the sleigh
　　Through the white and drifted snow.

Over the river and through the wood,—
　　Oh, how the wind does blow!
　　　　It stings the toes
　　　　And bites the nose
　　As over the ground we go.

Over the river and through the wood,
　　To have a first-rate play,
　　　　Hear the bells ring
　　　　" Ting-a-ling-ding! "
　　Hurrah for Thanksgiving Day!

Over the river and through the wood,
  Trot fast, my dapple gray!
    Spring over the ground
    Like a hunting hound!
  For this is Thanksgiving Day!

Over the river and through the wood,
  And straight through the barn-yard gate;
    We seem to go
    Extremely slow;
  It is so hard to wait!

Over the river and through the wood,
  Now grandmother's cap I spy!
    Hurrah for the fun!
    Is the pudding done?
  Hurrah for the pumpkin pie!

Forever on Thanksgiving Day

Wilbur D. Nesbit

LONG since the first fruits have been laid
  In plenitude before the shrine;
Long since the purple grapes have made
  The sacrifice of flame red wine —
And now across the empty field
  Which gleaning hands have left all bare,
Where harvest songs one time have pealed,
  The home path stretches, broad and fair.

The home path — O, the land is far
  That knows no path to lead us home!
The sky is strange that has no star
  To guide us whereso'er we roam;

The sea is sad that shows no wake
Of ships that seek the harbor bar
Whereon glad billows leap and break
And sing of where the home hearts are.

The eyes are blind that may not close
To conjure visions of the hearth
Where from a laughing firelight throws
Its glamour over heart-born mirth;
The ears are deaf that cannot hear
The home song pulsing in the air
In measures soft and sweet and clear —
The home song of the days back there.

For each the home path, be it street,
Or fair, broad highway, or the sea —
The path that lures the weary feet
To find where all the home things be.
What though one fares through lands away,
Or drifts or beats across the foam?
Forever on Thanksgiving Day
The heart will find the pathway home.

Quotations for Thanksgiving Day

God is glorified, not by our groans, but by our thanksgivings.— *Bishop Whittle.*

> I know not where His islands lift
>   Their fronded palms in air,
> I only know I cannot drift
>   Beyond His love and care.
>
>   — *John Greenleaf Whittier.*

> But let the good old crop adorn
>   The hills our fathers trod;
> Still let us for His golden corn,
>   Send up our thanks to God.
>
>   — *John Greenleaf Whittier.*

> Come, ye thankful people, come,
> Raise the song of Harvest-home,
> All is safely gathered in,
> Ere the winter storms begin.
>
>   — *Henry Alford.*

> Ay, call it holy ground,—
> The soil where first they trod!
> They have left unstained what there they found —
> Freedom to worship God!
>
>   — *Felicia Hemans.*

> Thank God for friends your life has known,
>   For every dear, departed day;
> The blessed past is safe alone —
>   God gives but does not take away;
> He only safely keeps above
>   For us the treasures that we love.
>
>   — *Phoebe Cary.*

> Come forth, come forth, with the chiming bell,
> A joyous throng to the altar's side;

Come mingle your tones with the organ's swell;
And, where the door of the feast stands wide,
Let the gray-haired sire to his grandchild tell
A tale of our nation's grateful pride.
— *Hannah E. Garey.*

Remember God's bounty in the year. String the pearls of His favor. Hide the dark parts, except so far as they are breaking out in light! Give this one day to thanks, to joy, to gratitude.— *Henry Ward Beecher.*

Oh! favors old, yet ever new;
    Oh! blessings with the sunshine sent.
The bounty overruns our due,
    The fullness shames our discontent.
— *John G. Whittier.*

So once in every year we throng
    Upon a day apart,
To praise the Lord with feast and song
    In thankfulness of heart.
— *Arthur Ginterman.*

Heap high the board with plenteous cheer and gather to the
        feast,
And toast that sturdy Pilgrim band whose courage never
        ceased.
Give praise to that All-Gracious
    One by whom their steps were led,
And thanks unto the harvest's
    Lord who sends our " daily bread."
— *Alice Williams Brotherton.*

For our country extending from sea to sea,
The land that is known as " The Land of the Free "—
    Thanksgiving! Thanksgiving!
— *Anonymous.*

CHRISTMAS DAY

December 25

Christmas is a Christian festival celebrated by every State, Territory and possession of the United States in memory of the birth of Jesus Christ. While December 25th was in all probability not the actual date of Christ's birth, that date was selected at first because the Romans celebrated this time of the year as a pagan festival. Therefore this day was chosen in early times in order to draw the Christian people away from the heathen festivities. They hoped to eventually purify or abolish these heathen customs and ideas. The day was first celebrated in the second century, it is said, by order of Telesphorus, seventh Bishop of Rome.

The Origin of Christmas

Anonymous

CHRISTMASS, a variation of Christmas, owes its name to
the fact that in the Roman churches a mass in honor of
Christ's birth was celebrated on that day. In many languages the word for Christmas means birthday, as the
French word Noël, the Italian Natale, and, indirectly,
the German Weihnachten, or sacred night, alluding to the
birth of Christ as the event that consecrated it. The
correct date of Christ's birth is unknown, nor was the day
observed as Christmas until two hundred years after his
birth, but Yuletide had been observed five hundred and
fifty years before, the Persians keeping the holiday very
much as we of the present day. Then Rome took up its
observance and borrowed customs from Egypt, Persia and
Greece, adopting also the mistletoe and its rites from
the Druids. Julius, pope of Rome in 400 A. D., fixed upon
the 25th of December as being the day of the winter sol-
stice, and to replace the pagan rites and festivals the
Church introduced grand masses or Christmasses. Grad-
ually came Christmas carols or Christmas hymns, then
Christmas trees and a revival or survival of the pagan
rites used with a Christian significance. Christmas now
has come to mean simply the day, whereas formerly it was
a season. Our English ancestors observed the holiday
for twelve days and nights, finishing with Twelfth Night.
In Ireland the little altar is kept up, with its candles and
decorations, until "Little Christmas Day," two weeks
from Christmas, and the Christmas decorations may be

left until Candlemas Day, the 2nd of February, when they must all be taken down unless the inmates wish to see a goblin for every leaf left on the wall.

Wherever the religion of Christ is accepted, the festival of the Christian Church — Christmas — is universally celebrated on the 25th of December, or the eve before, as the anniversary of the birth of the Savior. Christmas! What does the word mean? The first half consisting of the sacred name of the Savior is in the Greek word "kristos," which means "the anointed," and has the same meaning as the Hebrew "Messiah." The final syllable of Christmas —"mas" is evidently synonymous with the communion service — celebrated with great pomp and ceremony in Catholic places of worship upon the anniversary of our Savior's birth. The final "s" was cut off as unnecessary. This word "mass" is much the same in English, Italian, French, Danish, German, Spanish and Latin, and signifies the communion called the "Lord's supper." It is believed to have been derived from the words of dismissal at the close; "Ite missa est concio," or "Go, the assembly is dissolved."

Christmas Day

Margaret E. Sangster

Of all dear days is Christmas Day
    The dearest and the best,
Still on its dawn the angels sing
    Their songs of peace and rest.
And yet the blessed Christ-child comes
    And walks the shining way
Which brings to simple earthly homes
    Heaven's light on Christmas Day.

Then, deep in silent woods, the trees —
　　The hemlock, pine and fir —
Thrill to the chilly winter breeze,
　　And waft a breath of myrrh.
And far and near Kris Kringle's bells
　　Their airy music shake,
And dancing feet of boys and girls
　　A sweeter joyance make.

The Christ-Child came to Bethlehem,
　　To Mary's happy breast,
And found within her brooding arms
　　A warm, encircling nest.
And many a tiny, cherub child
　　In Mother's arms to-day
Smiles like the Christ, the undefiled,
　　On this dear Christmas Day.

The Christmas Spirit

Anonymous

WHAT is the Christmas spirit?

It is the spirit which brings a smile to the lips and tenderness to the heart; it is the spirit which warms one into friendship with all the world, which serves one to hold out the hand of fellowship to every man and woman, to every boy and girl.

For the Christmas motto is " Peace on earth, goodwill to men," and the spirit of Christmas demands that it ring in our hearts and find expression in kindly acts and loving words.

What a joyful thing for the world it would be if the Christmas spirit could do this, not only on that holiday, but on every day of the year. What a beautiful place the world would be to live in! Peace and good-will everywhere and always! Let each of us resolve that, so far as we are concerned, peace and good-will shall be our motto every day, and that we will do our best to make the Christmas spirit last all the year round.

Christmas

Nahum Tate

WHILE shepherds watched their flocks by night,
  All seated on the ground,
The angel of the Lord came down,
  And glory shone around.

" Fear not," said he (for mighty dread
  Had seized their troubled mind) ;
" Glad tidings of great joy I bring
  To you and all mankind.

" To you, in David's town, this day
  Is born of David's line
The Saviour who is Christ the Lord;
  And this shall be the sign:

" The heavenly Babe you there shall find
  To human view display'd,
All meanly wrapt in swathing bands,
  And in a manger laid."

Thus spake the Seraph; and forthwith
  Appear'd a shining throng
Of angels, praising God, and thus
  Address'd their joyful song:

" All glory be to God on high,
    And to the earth be peace;
Good-will henceforth from heaven to men
    Begin, and never cease ! "

The Shepherds

Laura Spencer Portor

THEY never sought; nay, they but woke and came
    Quickly; nor paused they to bring
    Gifts to the Little King; —
No gems had they, nor a remembered name.

E'en while they knelt, three Wise Men worshiping,
    Over the desert rode afar,
    Patient, and sought a star; —
Yet came too late to hear the angels sing.

Oh, wake us, make us simple, make us mild!
    Spare us the desert thirst and fears,
    The garnered gems, and years!
Oh, bring us to Thee quickly, Holy Child.

From *Harper's Magazine*.

Christmas Bells

Anonymous

" ARE you waking ? " shout the breezes
    To the tree tops waving high,
" Don't you hear the happy tidings
    Whispered to the earth and sky?

Have you caught them in your dreaming,
  Brook and rill in snowy dells?
Do you know the joy we bring you
  In the merry Christmas bells!

"Are you waking, flowers that slumber
  In the deep and frosty ground?
Do you hear what we are breathing,
  To the listening world around?
For we hear the sweetest story
  That the glad year ever tells:
How He loved the little children,—
  He who brought the Christmas bells!"
Ding, dong! ding, dong! Christmas bells!

Christmas Carol

Phillips Brooks

THE earth has grown old with its burden of care,
  But at Christmas it always is young,
The heart of the jewel burns lustrous and fair,
And its soul full of music bursts forth on the air,
  When the song of the angels is sung.

It is coming, Old Earth, it is coming to-night!
  On the snowflakes which cover thy sod
The feet of the Christ-child fall gentle and white,
And the voice of the Christ-child tells out with delight
  That mankind are the children of God.

On the sad and the lowly, the wretched and poor,
  The voice of the Christ-child shall fall;
And to every blind wanderer open the door

Of hope that he dared not to dream of before,
  With a sunshine of welcome for all.

The feet of the humblest may walk in the field
  Where the feet of the Holiest trod,
This, then, is the marvel to mortals revealed
When the silvery trumpets of Christmas have pealed,
  That mankind are the children of God.

Christmas Dusk

Wilbur D. Nesbit

COME, little boy, to mother's knee.
  The Christmas twilight trembles down
With rose-tints for the wondrous tree
  And rose-glow for the snow-clad town,
And all is marvelous — but you
  Most marvelous of all to me,
For I may hold you as I do,
  As Mary held Him on her knee.

And He was sweet and He was fair,
  As are all mothers' little boys;
His lips, His smile, His eyes, His hair,
  To Mary were her chiefest joys.
And she would sing to Him, as I
  Sing while the sun dies in the west;
I hear your weary, sleepy sigh
  As Mary heard His on her breast:

And in the after years, I think,
  When He was treading sorrow's way
And held the bitter cup to drink,
  She brooded on the happy day

When He was singing through the room
    And found a hundred things to do
To drive away all chance of gloom —
    And was a little boy, like you.

So drop your toys, and let us sing
    The songs that heart and home have blest,
For love is more than anything
    And life is work, and play, and rest.
And Mary's was the mother-heart,
    A heart of love all fair and fine
That into tender throbs could start
    For just a little boy, like mine.

Across the years I reach to her
    And touch her white and empty hands,
Down all the ages seems to stir
    A message that she understands,
The subtle rapture that I keep
    Shrined in the very soul of me
When I may hold you here, asleep,
    As Mary held Him on her knee.

Merry Christmas

Charles Dickens

Nephew: A Merry Christmas, Uncle! God save you!
Scrooge: Bah! Humbug!
Nephew: Christmas a humbug, Uncle! You don't
mean that, I am sure.
Scrooge: I do. Merry Christmas! What right have
you to be merry? What reason have you to be merry?
You're poor enough.

Nephew: (laughing) Come then! What right have you to be dismal? What reason have you to be morose? You're rich enough.

Scrooge: Bah! Humbug!

Nephew: Don't be cross, Uncle.

Scrooge: What else can I be, when I live in such a world of fools as this? Merry Christmas! Out upon Merry Christmas! What's Christmas time to you but a time for paying bills without money; a time for finding yourself a year older, and not an hour richer. If I could work my will, every idiot who goes about with " Merry Christmas " on his lips, should be boiled with his own pudding, and buried with a stake of holly run through his heart. He should!

Nephew: Uncle!

Scrooge: Nephew! Keep Christmas in your own way, and let me keep it in mine.

Nephew: Keep it! But you don't keep it.

Scrooge: Let me leave it alone, then. Much good may it do you! Much good it has ever done you!

Nephew: There are many things from which I might have derived good, by which I have not profited, I dare say, Christmas among the rest. But I am sure I have always thought of Christmas time as a good time; a kind, forgiving, charitable, pleasant time; the only time I know of, in the long calendar of the year, when men and women seem by one consent to open their shut-up hearts freely, and to think of people below them as if they really were fellow-passengers to the grave, and not another race of creatures bound on other journeys. And therefore, Uncle, though it has never put a scrap of gold or silver in my pocket, I believe that it has done me good, and will do me good; and I say, God bless it! — *Adapted.*

Christmas in the North

Margaret E. Sangster

FAR up in the Northern country,
　　Where the bitter storm-winds blow,
Till heaped on field and highway
　　Are the frozen drifts of snow;
In the dawn of merry Christmas,
　　Thatched roof and castle eaves,
Wall and turret and gateway
　　Laugh under nodding sheaves.
For he would be hard and thankless,
　　The churl whose heart and hand
Should be closed to the birds that linger
　　Like orphans in the land.
To lofty homes and lowly
　　They flock, a cheery train,
To scatter their songs of summer
　　O'er the feast of winter grain.
Within, the innocent children
　　Carol of Christmas Day,
And without, the little pensioners
　　Are busy and blithe as they.

The Little Christmas Tree

Susan Coolidge

THE Christmas Day was coming, the Christmas Eve drew
　　near,
The fir-trees, they were talking low at midnight, cold
　　and clear;

And this is what the fir-tree said, all in the pale moonlight:
" Now, which of us shall chosen be to grace the holy
night?"

The tall trees and the goodly trees raised each a lofty
head,
In glad and secret confidence, though not a word they
said.
But one, the baby of the band, could not restrain a sigh —
" You all will be approved," he said, " but oh! what
chance have I?

" I am so small, so very small, no one will mark or know
How thick and green my needles are, how true my
branches grow.
Few toys and candles could I hold, but heart and will
are free,
And in my heart of hearts I know I am a Christmas
tree."

The Christmas angel hovered near; he caught the grieving word,
And, laughing low, he hurried forth, with love and pity
stirred.
He sought and found St. Nicholas, the dear old Christmas saint,
And in his fatherly, kind ear rehearsed the fir-tree's
plaint.

Saints are all-powerful, we know, so it befell that day
That, axe on shoulder, to the grove a woodman took his
way.

One baby girl he had at home, and he went forth to
find
A little tree as small as she, just suited to his mind.

Oh! glad and proud the baby-fir, amid its brethren tall,
To be thus chosen and singled out, the first among them
all!
He stretched his fragrant branches, his little heart beat
fast;
He was a real Christmas tree — he had his wish at last.

One large and shining apple, with cheeks of ruddy gold;
Six tapers, and a tiny doll were all that he could hold.
The baby laughed, the baby crowed, to see the tapers
bright;
The forest baby felt the joy, and shared in the delight.

And when, at last, the tapers died, and when the baby
slept,
The little fir, in silent night, a patient vigil kept.
Though scorched and brown its needles were, it had no
heart to grieve;
"I have not lived in vain," he said, "thank God for
Christmas Eve!"

The Christ Child's Christmas

Laura Spencer Portor

"OH, Brother Christ, come play with me
And you shall share my Christmas tree;

Oh Little Brother Christ, you may
Have all these gifts of mine today;

" And what you will you may take home,
If you will come, if you will come."

And so the little Christ Child came
To him who called upon His name.

The glittering Christmas candles' light
Flickered and flared across the night;

Above, the waiting heavens were starr'd
But past them came the Little Lord;

The broken gift, the gilded ball,
The tinsel star, He loved them all,

And overhead, the angel train
Waited the Christ Child all in vain.

By permission of the *Woman's Home Companion.*

The Gift

Laura Spencer Portor

OH, there be many candles bright
Upon Thy tree on Christmas night;
What need that I should add a light!

Oh, there be many stars that shine
To make Thy Christmas heavens fine;
What need is there of gold of mine!

O Little Lord, O Little King,
With men and angels worshipping,
What gift is there that I could bring!

(The angels turned their eyes on me;
The Shepherd looked surprise on me;
The King flung cold surmise on me!)

" Give gifts," He said (and looked no blame!)
" Not unto Me, but in My name;
Tell someone why it was I came."

By permission of the *Woman's Home Companion.*

Is There a Santa Claus?

Charles A. Dana

As we grow older, we change our ideas concerning
things about us. Our ideals also change. These changes
cost us many a pang. Some of our beliefs may be dearer
than pets, or kinsfolk, or friends. Many men have died
for their beliefs. When we find we have been mistaken,
we must gather new ideas. It almost always happens that
our new ideas are better, nobler, and happier than our
outgrown fancies. An example of this is our first idea
of Santa Claus. We are fortunate if our early belief in
Santa Claus brings to us a true vision of the real Spirit
of Christmas, as it did for the author of the following
charming answer to a child's letter of inquiry. Mr.
Charles A. Dana was for many years one of the foremost journalists of America. He came to be editor
the New York *Sun* and while acting in this capacity received the following letter:

Dear Editor:
  I am eight years old. Some of my little friends say
that there is no Santa Claus. Please tell me the truth.
Is there a Santa Claus? VIRGINIA O. HANLON.

The great editor answered in the following editorial, full of the comprehension of the Spirit of Christmas Giving beyond the ken of most unthinking persons.

IS THERE A SANTA CLAUS?

Virginia, your little friends are wrong. They have been affected by the skepticism of a skeptical age. They think that nothing can be which is not comprehensible by their little minds. They do not believe except they see. All minds, Virginia, whether they be men's or children's, are little. In this great universe of ours, man is a mere insect, an ant, in his intellect, compared with the boundless worlds about him, as measured by the intelligence capable of grasping the whole truth and knowledge.

Yes, Virginia, there is a Santa Claus. He exists as certainly as love and generosity and devotion exist, and you know that they abound and give to your life its highest beauty and joy. Alas, how dreary the world would be if there were no Santa Claus! It would be as dreary as if there were no Virginias! There would be no childlike faith, then, no poetry, no romance, to make tolerable this existence. We should have no enjoyment except in sense and sight. The eternal light with which childhood fills the world would then be extinguished.

Not to believe in Santa Claus! You might as well not believe in fairies! You might get your papa to hire men to watch all the chimneys on Christmas Eve to catch Santa Claus; but even if they did not see Santa Claus coming down, what would that prove? Not everybody sees Santa Claus. The most real things in the world are those that neither children nor men see. Did you ever see fairies dancing on the lawn? Of course not; but that's no proof that they were not there. No one can conceive or imagine all the things that are unseen or unsee-able in the world.

You may tear apart a baby's rattle and see what makes the noise inside, but there is a veil covering the unseen world that not the strongest man, not even the united strength of all the strongest men that ever lived, could tear apart. Only faith, fancy, poetry, love, romance, can push aside that curtain and view and picture the supernal beauty and glory beyond. It is all real. Ah, Virginia, in all the world there is nothing else real and abiding.

No Santa Claus? Thank God, he lives, and he lives forever! A thousand years from now, Virginia, nay, ten thousand years from now, he will continue to make glad the hearts of children.

Santa Claus

Anonymous

HE comes in the night! He comes in the night!
  He softly, silently comes;
While the little brown heads on the pillows so white
  Are dreaming of bugles and drums.
He cuts through the snow like a ship through the foam,
  While the white flakes around him whirl;
Who tells him I know not, but he findeth the home
  Of each good little boy and girl.

His sleigh it is long, and deep, and wide;
  It will carry a host of things,
While dozens of drums hang over the side,
  With the sticks sticking under the strings:
And yet not the sound of a drum is heard,
  Not a bugle blast is blown,

As he mounts to the chimney-top like a bird,
  And drops to the hearth like a stone.

The little red stockings he silently fills,
  Till the stockings will hold no more;
The bright little sleds for the great snow hills
  Are quickly set down on the floor.
Then Santa Claus mounts to the roof like a bird,
  And glides to his seat in the sleigh;
Not the sound of a bugle or drum is heard
  As he noiselessly gallops away.

He rides to the East, and he rides to the West,
  Of his goodies he touches not one;
He eateth the crumbs of the Christmas feast
  When the dear little folks are done.
Old Santa Claus doeth all that he can;
  This beautiful mission is his;
Then, children, be good to the little old man,
  When you find who the little man is.

A Visit from St. Nicholas

Clement C. Moore

'TWAS the night before Christmas, when all through the
    house
Not a creature was stirring, not even a mouse;
The stockings were hung by the chimney with care,
In hopes that St. Nicholas soon would be there;
The children were nestled all snug in their beds,
While visions of sugar-plums danced through their heads;
And mamma in her kerchief, and I in my cap,
Had just settled our brains for a long winter's nap,—

When out on the lawn there arose such a clatter,
I sprang from my bed to see what was the matter,
Away to the window I flew like a flash,
Tore open the shutters and threw up the sash.
The moon, on the breast of the new-fallen snow,
Gave a luster of midday to objects below;
When what to my wondering eyes should appear,
But a miniature sleigh and eight tiny reindeer,
With a little old driver, so lively and quick,
I knew in a moment it must be St. Nick.
More rapid than eagles his coursers they came,
And he whistled and shouted and called them by name:
" Now, Dasher! now, Dancer! Now, Prancer and Vixen!
On, Comet! on, Cupid! on, Donder and Blitzen!
To the top of the porch, to the top of the wall!
Now, dash away, dash away, dash away all! "
As dry leaves that before the wild hurricane fly,
So, up to the house-top the coursers they flew,
With a sleigh full of toys,— and St. Nicholas too.
And then in a twinkling I heard on the roof
The prancing and pawing of each little hoof.
As I drew in my head and was turning around,
Down the chimney St. Nicholas came with a bound.
He was dressed all in fur from his head to his foot,
And his clothes were all tarnished with ashes and soot;
A bundle of toys he had flung on his back,
And he looked like a peddler just opening his pack.
His eyes, how they twinkled! his dimples, how merry!
His cheeks were like roses, his nose like a cherry;
His droll little mouth was drawn up like a bow,
And the beard on his chin was as white as the snow.
The stump of a pipe he held tight in his teeth,
And the smoke it encircled his head like a wreath.
He had a broad face, and a little round belly

That shook, when he laughed, like a bowl full of jelly.
He was chubby and plump,— a right jolly old elf,—
And I laughed when I saw him, in spite of myself.
A wink of his eye and a twist of his head
Soon gave me to know I had nothing to dread.
He spoke not a word, but went straight to his work,
And filled all the stockings; then turned with a jerk,
And laying a finger aside of his nose,
And giving a nod, up the chimney he rose.
He sprang to his sleigh, to his team gave a whistle,
And away they all flew like the down of a thistle;
But I heard him exclaim, ere he drove out of sight:
" Happy Christmas to all, and to all a good-night!"

Kriss Kringle

Thomas Bailey Aldrich

Just as the moon was fading
    Amid her misty rings,
And every stocking was stuffed
    With childhood's precious things,

Old Kriss Kringle looked around,
    And saw on the elm-tree bough,
High hung, an oriole's nest,
    Lonely and empty now.

" Quite a stocking," he laughed,
    " Hung up there on a tree!
I didn't suppose the birds
    Expected a present from me!"

Then old Kriss Kringle, who loves
  A joke as well as the best,
Dropped a handful of snowflakes
  Into the oriole's empty nest.

The Angels' Song

Edmund Hamilton Sears

IT came upon the midnight clear,
  That glorious song of old,
From angels bending near the earth
  To touch their harps of gold:
"Peace to the earth, good-will to men
  From heaven's all-gracious King!"
The world in solemn stillness lay
  To hear the angels sing.

Still through the cloven skies they come,
  With peaceful wings unfurled;
And still their heavenly music floats
  O'er all the weary world:
Above its sad and lowly plains
  They bend on heavenly wing,
And ever o'er its Babel sounds
  The blessed angels sing.

Yet with the woes of sin and strife
  The world has suffered long;
Beneath the angel-strain have rolled
  Two thousand years of wrong;
And man, at war with man, hears not
  The love-song which they bring:
O, hush the noise, ye men of strife,
  And hear the angels sing!

And ye, beneath life's crushing load
　　Whose forms are bending low;
Who toil along the climbing way
　　With painful steps and slow,—
Look now! for glad and golden hours
　　Come swiftly on the wing;
O, rest beside the weary road,
　　And hear the angels sing.

For lo! the days are hastening on,
　　By prophet-bards foretold,
When with the ever-circling years
　　Comes round the age of gold;
When Peace shall over all the earth
　　Its ancient splendors fling,
And the whole world send back the song
　　Which now the angels sing.

Quotations for Christmas Day

　　We hear the Christmas angels
　　　　The great, glad tidings tell.
　　Oh, come to us, abide with us,
　　　　Our Lord Emmanuel.
　　　　　　　　　— *Phillips Brooks.*

The best of Christmas joy,
Dear little girl or boy,
That comes on that merry-making day,
Is the happiness of giving
To another child that's living
Where Santa Claus has never found his way.
　　　　　　　　　— *Youth's Companion.*

Ring, O bells, in gladness,
Tell of joy to-day;

Ring and swing o'er all the world so wide.
Banish thoughts of sadness,
Drive all grief away,
For it is the Merry Christmas-tide.

— Alice Jean Cleator.

The yearly course that brings this day about,
Shall never see it but a holiday.

— William Shakespeare.

Sing the song of great joy, that the angels began,
Sing the glory to God, and of good-will to man.

— John G. Whittier.

Again at Christmas did we weave
The holly round the Christmas hearth.

— Alfred Tennyson.

Sing, O my heart!
Sing thou in rapture this dear morn
Whereon the blessed Prince is born.

— Eugene Field.

Heap on more wood! the wind is chill!
But let it whistle as it will,
We'll keep our merry Christmas still.

— Sir Walter Scott.

"What means that star," the shepherds said,
"That brightens through the rocky glen?"
And angels, answering overhead,
Sang, "Peace on earth, good-will to men."

— James Russell Lowell.

For the Christ-child who comes is the Master of all;
No palace too great, and no cottage too small.

— Phillips Brooks.

Celestial choirs from courts above
Shed sacred glories there;

And angels with their sparkling lyres
　　Make music on the air.
　　　　　　　　　　— Edmund H. Sears.

Hail the heaven-born Prince of Peace!
Hail the Sun of Righteousness!
Light and life to all he brings,
Risen with healing in his wings.
　　　　　　　　　　— John Wesley.

Happy, happy Christmas, that can win us back to the
delusions of our childish days, that can recall to the old man
the pleasures of his youth, and transport the sailor and the
traveler, thousands of miles away, back to his own fireside
and his quiet home! — *Charles Dickens.*

The merry Christmas, with its generous boards,
　Its fire-lit hearths, and gifts and blazing trees,
Its pleasant voices uttering gentle words,
Its genial mirth, attuned to sweet accords,
Its holiest memories!
The fairest season of the passing year —
The merry, merry Christmas time is here.
　　　　　　　　　　— George Arnold.

Oh! lovely voices of the sky
Which hymned the Saviour's birth,
Are ye not singing still on high,
Ye that sang, " Peace on earth? "
To us yet speak the strains
Wherewith, in time gone by,
Ye blessed the Syrian swains,
Oh, voices of the sky!
　　　　　　　　　　— Felicia Hemans.

Sing, O my heart!
Sing thou in rapture this dear morn
Whereon the blessed Prince is born.
　　　　　　　　　　— Eugene Field.

O earth, O heart, be glad on this glad morn!
God is with man! Life, life to us is born!
— Lucy Larcom.

Then sing to the holly, the Christmas holly,
  That hangs over peasant and king;
While we laugh and carouse
  'Neath its glittering boughs,
To the Christmas holly we'll sing.
— Eliza Cook.

  Good luck unto old Christmas,
    And long life let us sing,
  For he doth more good unto the poor
    Than many a crownéd king!
— Mary Howitt.

A Christmas gambol oft could cheer
The poor man's heart through half the year.
— Sir Walter Scott.

SPEAKERS

There is a constant demand for new material for public speaking in schools and colleges, or before societies and political gatherings and for voice training and declamation contests. We have made a specialty of books of this character for many years and have listed below a large variety of Speakers for every need and for every occasion.

Ashley's 50 Orations That Have Won Prizes in Speaking Contests *(Just Published)* - 2.00

This book contains the Winning Orations of the Interstate Oratorical Association and other Intercollegiate Speaking Contests. It is the most comprehensive material for declamatory contestants that has ever been assembled in a single volume.

Blackstone's The Best American Orations of Today - - - - - - - - 2.00

It has been the aim of the compiler to embody in this volume the best thoughts of leading Americans—men who stand as the highest types of honesty, intelligence, and useful citizenship—for the emulation of the youth of our land.

Among the noted men represented in this volume are: Rev. Dr. S. Parkes Cadman, Edward W. Bok, Nicholas Murray Butler, Calvin Coolidge, Charles G. Dawes, Elbert H. Gary, David Starr Jordan, William H. Taft, Warren G. Harding, Rt. Rev. Wm. T. Manning, Robert M. La Follette, Herbert Clark Hoover, William E. Borah, William Jennings Bryan, Stephen S. Wise, Charles Evans Hughes, Albert J. Beveridge, Chauncey M. Depew, Theodore Roosevelt and Elihu Root.

Craig and Gunnison's Pieces That Have
Taken Prizes in Speaking Contests - - 2.00

The best collection of *Prize Winning* Pieces ever published. The compilers spent nearly three years in collecting the pieces for this book. All have actually taken one or more prizes in some Prize Speaking Contest.

Among the selections will be found: The Aspirations of the American People; The Storming of Mission Ridge; Opportunities of the Scholar; The Elements of National Wealth; Duty of Literary Men to America; Love of Country; Best Policy in Regard to Naturalization; Truth and Victory; True Courage; Freedom and Patriotism; The Pilot's Story; The Yacht Race; The Chariot Race; Siege of the Alamo; The Unknown Rider; Waterloo; The Present Age.

Blackstone's New Pieces That Will Take
Prizes in Speaking Contests - - - - - 2.00

To satisfy the constantly increasing demand for *New Pieces* for Prize Speaking Contests, the compiler (with the permission of the authors and publishers) has adapted a number of the choicest selections from the most celebrated works of our best known writers. Each selection is especially suited for Prize Speaking Contests.

Neil's The Sources of Effectiveness
In Public Speaking* - - - - - - - 2.60

A practical handbook for the development of ability to construct and present a successful speech. It gives us a new conception of the study of speech. The author goes straight to the bottom of the matter, as no other writer on this subject has done, and enables the speaker, professional or non-professional, to find and develop the sources of full effectiveness in speaking.

2

Shurter and Watkins' New Poems That Will Take Prizes in Speaking Contests   2.00

Contains an exceptionally fine collection of classical poetry and poems by contemporary authors. All these pieces have been selected because of their suitability for prize speaking contests. A head-note preceding each poem gives brief suggestions as to the best method of delivering it.

This list comprises poems by Constance D'Arcy Mackay; Corinne Roosevelt Robinson; Theodosia Garrison Faulks; Robert Frost; Hamlin Garland; John Gould Fletcher; Eunice Tietjens; Wilfrid Wilson Gibson; Chester Firkins; Badger Clark; Arthur Chapman; Ruth Comfort Mitchell Young; Alan Seeger; Robert William Service; Hermann Hagedorn; Edgar Lee Masters; Angela Morgan; William Rose Benét; Witter Bynner; Harriet Monroe; Charles Hanson Towne; Florence Earle Coates; Eva Rose York; Edward Forrester Sutton; John Augustus Gilkey; William Lawrence Chittenden; Anna Hempstead Branch; Jean Starr Untermeyer and others.

McHale's Pieces That Have Won Prizes in Speaking Contests - - - - - - 2.00

This volume contains over 150 selections that have won prizes in Speaking Contests. Among the number being Clean Politics (Roosevelt), The Nation's Need of Men (Jordan), Lasca (Desprez), The Soul of the Violin (Merrill), Gunga Din (Kipling), The Last Hymn, The Vagabonds (Trowbridge), The Sermon (Alcott), Permanent Peace (Saretsky), A Second Trial (Kellogg), The Arena Scene from Quo Vadis (Sienkiewicz), A Hero of the Furnace Room, etc.

In addition to these *"prize winners"* there are a number of excellent Encore Pieces, mostly humorous.

3

Shurter's Winning Declamations—How To
Speak Them - - - - - - - 2.00

A collection of many brief declamations of famous speakers and writers. Each selection has an introductory paragraph suggesting the best method of interpretation and delivery.

In addition there is a chapter telling *"How to Become a Successful Public Speaker."*

Shurter and Watkins' Masterpieces of
Modern Verse* - - - - - - - - 1.50

This book will prove a great boon to all persons who are interested in new material for reading or for public speaking. Only *modern poetry* has been included, because the modern poets are closer to the hearts of all of us, both in style and choice of subject matter. Each poem is

preceded by a head-note containing a short biographical sketch of the author and brief suggestions as to the best means of interpretation.

Among the famous poets represented in this book are: Henry Van Dyke; John Masefield; Louis Untermeyer; Edwin Markham; Richard LeGallienne; Bliss Carman; Edna St. Vincent Millay; Helen Hoyt; Joyce Kilmer; Katharine Lee Bates; Elias Lieberman; Clinton Scollard; Cale Young Rice; Louis Imogen Guiney; Alfred Noyes; Berton Braley; John Drinkwater; John Hall Wheelock; Richard Hovey; Adelaide Crapsey.

Well-selected poems from over sixty modern British and American authors, arranged for the use of public-speaking or the interpretative-reading class. Each poem is preceded by a brief biographical and suggestive foreword. "Nature," "The City and Modern Life," "Home Life and Childhood," "Reflective and Inspirational," and "Especially Musical" are some of the organization headings.

—The English Journal.

Deming and Bemis' Pieces for Every Day
The Schools Celebrate - - - - - - 2.00

Here you will find *New Selections* for all the days the schools celebrate including New Year's Day, Lincoln's Birthday, Washington's Birthday, Arbor and Bird Day, Mother's Day, Memorial Day, Flag Day, Independence Day, Labor Day, Constitution Day, Columbus Day, Roosevelt Day, Armistice Day, Thanksgiving Day, Christmas Day.

Niemeier's New Plays for Every Day The
Schools Celebrate *(Just Published)* - 2.00

A collection of new original plays for every day the schools celebrate. Full stage directions are given, the characters named, and all needed information regarding the costumes required and how to make them.

Contents: The Joys of the New Year; Choosing a Statue for Lincoln Park; George Washington at the Helm of State; Arbor Day or Bird Day in the Woods; The Homemaker and Her Aids; The Veteran's Story; Our Country's Flag; The Adoption of the Declaration; The Meaning of Labor Day; News of the Adoption of the Constitution; The Way to India; Thanksgiving Time in Plymouth; A Visit from Mr. and Mrs. Santa Claus; A Junior Red Cross Pageant; One Country, One Flag, One Language; The New Patriotism.

Fry's Educational Dramatics* - - - - - .75

If you want to teach whatever you are teaching, with renewed enthusiasm, if you want to put on plays at once entertaining and educationally significant, if you want to know all about the Dramatic Instinct and how and why to use it, this book will help you.

5

Gunnison's New Dialogues and Plays - - 2.50
(Primary, Intermediate and Advanced)

These new dialogues and plays are adapted from the very best literature and gathered from the most recent sources. One of the features of this book is the carefully prepared introduction to each dialogue. Not only are the characters named in order of importance, but the stage settings, the characteristics of the actors, the costumes, the relation of one to another, age, size, etc., are all mentioned.

LeRow's Pieces for Every Occasion - - 2.00

A collection of popular pieces suitable for Lincoln's Birthday, Washington's Birthday, Arbor Day, Flag Day, Easter, May Day, Memorial Day, Graduation and Closing Days, Fourth of July, Thanksgiving, Christmas, New Year's Day, and many other public occasions. *Very few, if any, of these pieces will be found in other books.* Several pages of Quotations for Every Occasion have recently been added.

Lovejoy and Adams' Pieces for Every Month of the Year - - - - - 2.00

Selections for children 6 to 15 years of age, dealing with nature and children's activities. You will find in this new book pieces to speak that are suitable for every day of the year beginning with the Spring months. There are pieces relating to the Sun, Wind, Rain, Clouds, Stars, Moon,

Seeds, Grass, Birds, Trees, Flowers, Meadows, Butterflies, Bees, Fairies, Jack Frost.

This is the most complete collection of poetry relating to Nature ever published. The scheme of nature study as outlined in the school work of the year has been carefully followed.

Pearson's Humorous Speaker - - - - - 2.00

Every person who achieves to success as a public speaker or reader ought to have this book. Here you will find the kind of pieces that will *"bring down the house"* with peals of side-splitting laughter. Only selections by the best authors have been included, such as Riley, Jerome, Kipling, Mark Twain, and other equally well-known Humorists.

The collection has the distinction of having admitted in no case the doubtfully laughable. Where fun is best *"The Humorous Speaker"* is best.

Scott's Psychology of Public Speaking* - - 1.60

Written by Walter Dill Scott, President of the Northwestern University. A study of how to become an effective public speaker or debater and how to sway, and persuade an audience.

Contents: Mental Imagery, Mental Imagery in Public Speaking. Modern Theories of the Emotions. Emotions and Their Expressional Control. Emotions and Their Proper Expressional Methods. Darwin and Wundt's Principles of Emotional Expressions. The Fluctuation of Attention. Rhythm. Rhythm in Written and Oral Discourse. Suggestion. Rendering an Audience Suggestible. Psychology of the Crowd and of the Audience. Memory. Practical Applications of the Psychology of Memory. Bibliography.

Pearson & Hicks' Extemporaneous Speaking* 2.00

This book gives a working method for preparing to speak, an appreciation of what is required in effective extemporaneous speaking, and an acquaintance with modern examples for practice.